"Don't ever touch me again. I hate you!"

Dawn backed away from her husband and continued bitterly. "I know now why you married me, Sebastian. Because an innocent young wife would be an asset to your political career." Her voice rose hysterically. "And because you wanted to use me to conceal your sordid affair with another woman!"

"*Dios!*" He spoke hoarsely. "I thought you understood—that you realized—" he broke off, his expression suddenly freezing into harsh, bitter lines. "May I remind you that you didn't have to marry me. But you wanted to make sure I would help you locate your sister. Well, I will fulfill my part of the bargain." He moved threateningly nearer. "And now, you will fulfill yours!"

D1315565

Other titles by

FLORA KIDD
IN HARLEQUIN PRESENTS

Other titles by

FLORA KIDD
IN HARLEQUIN ROMANCES

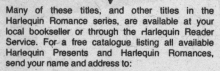

FLORA KIDD

marriage in mexico

Harlequin Books

TORONTO • LONDON • NEW YORK • AMSTERDAM
SYDNEY • HAMBURG • PARIS

Harlequin Presents edition published August 1979
ISBN 0-373-70804-1

Original hardcover edition published in 1978
by Mills & Boon Limited

CHAPTER ONE

ONLY the distant sound of surf falling on an unseen shore, coming through the slightly open window, saved the room from being completely silent and only the pool of rosy light cast by a standard lamp saved it from being completely dark.

On a wide bed which was canopied and flounced with sea-green silk a young woman lay on her back. She was covered up to her armpits. The skin of her bare arms and shoulders gleamed like ivory against the green silk of the sheets and pillows and the flaxen hair which fanned out from her head sparkled here and there with silvery light. Her eyes were closed, their long dark lashes sweeping down into the faint violet shadows beneath.

Suddenly her mouth quivered and she moaned, turning her head restlessly on the pillow. She was regaining consciousness slowly and reliving the moments of terror she had experienced that afternoon when she had been grasped and hurled into the thundering surf of the Pacific Ocean.

Once again she could hear the wild laughter of the young men who had taken hold of her. She could feel their rough hands on her arms, bruising and dragging, as they had forced her into the sea. Then she was being sucked down under roaring green water. Its saltiness was in her mouth and nose, stinging her eyes and filling her ears. Feeling as if her lungs would burst she struck out, arms and legs, flailing weakly in the surging sea. She struggled to the surface to gasp for breath, only to be

slapped in the face by the splintering white foam of another long breaker. Again she was sucked down, down
and down into darkness.

She opened her eyes and saw a graceful arch curving
over a window. Her eyes widening with surprise, she
looked around. She was in a room she had never seen
before; a lovely gracious room where glossy furniture
gleamed in the lamplight and a large black-haired woman
who was wearing a black dress and white apron sat in a
high-backed sewing chair close to a standard lamp, con-
centrating on her embroidery.

The young woman stretched and felt the slither of silk
over her body. Lifting the covers, she slid a hand beneath
them and touched herself. She was without a stitch of
clothing. She raised her head slightly and tried to speak.
Her voice made only a faint sound in the silence of the
room, but the other woman heard it. Putting her embroidery on a small table, she left the chair and came
across to stand beside the bed.

'*Como esta usted, señorita?*' she asked. Her dark
slightly slanted eyes were wary and no smile lightened
the sombreness of her broad Mexican face.

The young woman stared. She had not understood a
word the other woman had said and panic flickered
through her.

'Where am I?' she whispered in English. 'What is this
place?'

The dark-haired woman frowned fiercely and her eyes
flashed. She burst into a torrent of Mexican–Spanish, her
plump hands gesturing wildly. The young woman's panic
increased and she seemed to shrink into the bed.

'I don't understand,' she said plaintively. 'I don't understand you.'

The Mexican woman gave an exclamation of impatience, flung up her hands in a gesture of surrender and swinging round went from the room through an arched doorway.

Left alone, the young woman pushed with her elbows against the mattress of the bed in an attempt to sit up. Her head whirled and she fell back against the pillows. Eyes closed, she tried to remember why she was in bed in that strange room, but her brain seemed to be full of fog and she had a great longing to drift off to sleep.

The sound of a man's voice speaking the language the woman had spoken roused her slightly, but she didn't open her eyes. Then all was silent again and she was just floating off into sleep when she felt something touch her cheek. Someone was stroking it with a lean, hard finger.

'Don't go to sleep, little one, not yet,' said a cool masculine voice which spoke English with just the slightest of fascinating accents, a slurring of consonants and a lengthening of vowels. 'It's important that I know who you are.'

She opened her eyes and looked up into eyes which were as golden as an eagle's and just about as clear and hard. They were set in a lean sun-tanned face on either side of a dominant high-bridged nose and above them fine dark eyebrows followed the curve of the bone which arched over each of them.

'Who are you?' she whispered.

A faint smile lifted the corners of his wide broad-lipped mouth and was reflected briefly in his eyes. Then it had gone and he was staring down at her coldly.

'We could go on like this forever asking one another who the other is,' he said. 'But since this is my house, I have first go. Tell me, who are you?'

He was sitting on the edge of the bed very close to her. Thick damp black hair clustered about his high forehead and grew down the sides of his lean cheeks. His shoulders were wide under a crisp white evening shirt which was unbuttoned at the neck and part way down the front and she could see the shimmer of a golden chain against the sun-dark skin of his chest.

There was a formidable air of authority about him which disturbed her. Who was she? The fog swirled into her mind again and for a terrifying moment she couldn't remember anything. Then a name came to her like a gleam of light slanting through the fog.

'I think I'm Dawn,' she muttered.

His mouth took on an unpleasant, cruel curve and his eyes narrowed. Gold cuff links glittered briefly as he folded his arms across his chest and she caught the glint of a gold watch on a dark wrist beneath a white cuff.

'You *think*,' he jeered. 'Now don't tell me you've lost your memory. If you have the faster I have you out of here and in the psychiatric ward of the hospital the better.' His eyes glittered with a cold sardonic light as their glance roved over her hair, lingered on her eyes, then swept down insolently over her throat and shoulders to the fold of sheet barely covering her breasts.

'Dawn,' he drawled. 'It is, I suppose, an appropriate name for someone with your colouring—silver-gilt hair and silvery grey eyes. Is that why you chose it?'

The hostility in his manner rasped on her like a steel file, sharpening her wits so that she suddenly knew exactly who she was.

'I didn't choose it. It's my baptismal name,' she retorted, raising her head slightly.

'Dawn what?' he rapped.

'Dawn Aylwin.'

'So at last we make some progress. Dawn Aylwin from where? You're not Mexican, that much is obvious.

You're from north of the border, aren't you?'

Again fog swirled through her mind and she lay back and closed her eyes. North of the border? Which border? With slender fingers she rubbed her forehead trying to ease the throb that was there.

'I think. . . .' she began vaguely.

'Listen, *chiquita*,' the cool voice interrupted her. 'I'm not much interested in what you *think*. This act of yours may go over big with your friends way back home, but it isn't making any impression on me.'

'It isn't an act,' she spluttered furiously, and reached up in the bed. The bedclothes fell away from her, revealing her slender high-breasted body. His glance flashed down and she gasped, grabbed the sheet and clutched it to her with one hand to cover herself. 'I'm confused, that's all, and it's taking me time to remember. You're not helping by being so . . . so bossy.'

'I'm bossy,' he retorted equably, 'because I want to know the town, the state and if possible the number and name of the street where you usually live so that I can contact your family, tell them that you are safe. . . .'

'There isn't anyone you can contact,' she mumbled.

'What? No doting parents?'

'No. My mother died when I was quite small, when we lived in Ireland. After her death Dad decided to emigrate to Canada. He . . . he. . . .' Her voice trembled and she had to pause. 'He died a few weeks ago, in Toronto,' she went on. 'That's why I'm looking for Judy. Dad told me to find her. He was worried about her.'

'And who is Judy?'

She glanced at him searchingly. His handsome face was unrevealing, his eyes hard and steady.

'My sister,' she said.

'Why are you looking for her on this coast? What

would she be doing here? Touring?'

'I . . . I . . . don't know. Last time she wrote to us she gave us an address in Los Angeles.'

'When was that?'

'Six months ago. She was very pleased because she had managed to get a small part in a film. Dad and I were going to fly out to see her, but he became ill. I wrote to her asking her to come back to Toronto to see him. But she didn't write and she didn't come.' Tears of weakness welled in her eyes at the memory of those last few weeks of her father's life and she lay back again. 'After he died,' she went on, 'I drew out my savings and went out to L. A.'

'And she wasn't at the address she had given you,' he added, dryly. 'Isn't that how the story continues?'

She glanced at him warily. The curve to his mouth was cynical and scepticism gleamed in his eyes.

'If you're not going to believe me I don't see why I should tell you any more,' she snapped, anger flaring up in her.

'What did you do when you couldn't find her?' he asked, ignoring her protest.

'I went to the film studios where she said she'd worked,' she muttered woodenly. 'No one there seemed to know where she was. Then I met Farley.' Her mind cleared suddenly with the mention of the name. She sat up again, remembering to hug the sheet about her and glanced about the room as if expecting to see a tall young man with sun-gilt skin, blond hair and blue eyes step out of the shadows. 'Where is he?' she demanded, turning on the man who was sitting so close to her and who in his dark satanic way was so different from the young man who had befriended her. 'Where's Farley?'

'I have no idea,' he drawled.

Suspicion mushroomed inside her as she stared at him.

'What is this place, and who are you?' she demanded huskily. 'What have you done with my clothes and my money?' Then as he continued to stare at her something seemed to burst inside her. Forgetting to hold the concealing sheet about her, she clenched her hands and beat at his shoulder. 'Tell me, tell me,' she cried. 'Where is Farley? What have you done with him? Where is he? Where is he?'

All the anxiety of the past two months, the illness and death of her father, the search for her sister, had taken their toll of her mental stamina. And now Farley had gone too and she was with this cold-eyed, devilish stranger who asked so many questions and who was impervious to her appeals. Tears spurted from her eyes and sobs shook her. She stopped beating him and covered her face with her hands while she wept, for her dead father, her lost sister and her lost friend.

Arms, strong and tensile, came about her and she was drawn against the warmth of a hard body, sheathed in silk. Hands stroked her back soothingly and a voice spoke softly in her ear.

'Now, now, *chiquita*, take it easy, calm down.'

He rocked her gently as if she were a child and slowly her sobs subsided. With her head against his shoulder she lay limply, feeling the heat of his sun-tanned skin burning against hers through the thin silk of his shirt. He smelt of the sun and the sea and a little of the fragrance of cologne, and as she leaned against him a strange wish formed in her mind. Being held by him was the closest to heaven she had ever been, she thought hazily, and she wished she could stay there for ever.

But he was pushing her away from him, easing her back against the pillows. He lifted the sheet and covered her with it, tucking it in under her armpits, and once again she felt he was treating her as he might treat a child who had been left in his care for a short time.

'If I knew where Farley is right now and where your clothes and money are I wouldn't have to ask you questions, would I?' he said, coolly impersonal. 'Neither he nor your belongings were on the beach when I brought you ashore.'

'You brought me ashore?' she whispered, her eyes opening wide.

'Si,' he replied. 'You remember being in the ocean?' She nodded and a long shudder shook her from head to foot.

'I was surf-riding....' he began.

'Oh, I remember seeing you!' she interrupted, a smile curving her lips and her wet eyes glowing with remembered pleasure. 'You were a long way out, riding the waves like some dark god of the sea....' She broke off, a flush of embarrassment staining her cheeks when she saw his eyebrows lift and his eyes glint mockingly at her description of him. She turned her face away from him, feeling her body fill with a strange pulsing heat as she realised he had held her in his arms twice, once when he had brought her ashore and just now when she had been completely bare.

'I came across you one of the times you surfaced,' he went on. 'You were bobbing about like a piece of flotsam and I lost a good surfboard when I dived in to grab you before you could sink again. I managed to give you some mouth-to-mouth respiration to get you breathing again, then carried you to the beach and up here to the house.' He paused, then added crisply, 'Why were you trying to drown yourself?'

She turned her head quickly on the pillow to glance at him with surprise.

'I wasn't,' she denied.

'Then what happened?'

'They ... they threw me in,' she said, and again she shuddered.

'Who did?'

'Brett, Farley's friend, and another man. They'd all known one another before and were having a party.'

'Mmm. I saw them and heard them.' His mobile mouth grimaced in disgust. 'They were all pretty high on something.' The hard eyes considered her closely. 'Were you?' he rapped. 'Is that why you couldn't swim?'

'No, oh, no. They tried to make me take some sort of drug ... I don't know what it was, but I got away from them. Then they chased me and caught me. They dragged me towards the sea. I screamed at them to let go of me because I'm not a very strong swimmer and I was frightened of the surf. But they wouldn't listen to me. It was horrible, horrible!' She moved her head from side to side on the pillow, trying to shake off the nightmare feeling.

'Where did you meet this Farley?'

'In L. A. At the film studio. He'd been working there as an extra in a film and when he heard me asking about Judy he came up to me and told me he'd known her quite well. He showed me a photograph of her which he said she had given him. She had written on the back of it. He said he hadn't seen her for a while and was worried about her.' Dawn plucked at the sheet with her fingers. 'I liked him,' she muttered defensively, avoiding his eyes. 'He was kind and helpful when I most needed kindness and help.'

'Did he know where you might find your sister?'

'He said he believed she might be in Mexico, with a movie director who has a residence somewhere in the area of Manzanillo.'

'And did he know the name of the movie director?'

'Yes. Roberto Suarez. Have you heard of him?' She watched him closely for the slightest change in expression. But his face remained as impassive as that of an Aztec idol carved out of stone of which she had once seen pictures in a magazine.

'*Si*, I've heard of him,' he replied coolly. 'So what did your kind and helpful friend suggest then?'

She didn't like the sarcasm in his voice and showed her dislike by giving him an underbrowed glare which he returned with a mocking glint.

'He suggested that if I'd like to hire a car he and his friend Brett would come with me to help me find Roberto Suarez's house, and I agreed,' she said stiffly.

'How long had you known him before you agreed to such a suggestion?' he demanded.

'Four days.'

'*Por dios!*' he exclaimed. 'You must be very naïve.' His glance raked her as if he would have stripped the skin from her to find her soul. 'Didn't anyone ever tell you to beware of strange men?' he mocked.

'Farley wasn't a stranger. At least he didn't seem like one because he had known Judy, could talk about her and the things they'd done together,' she retorted, her eyes dark and stormy in her pale face. 'You're the stranger,' she accused. 'It's you I should beware of.'

His eyebrows tilted provocatively and he leaned towards her threateningly.

'But of course you should beware of me,' he taunted softly. 'I'm very dangerous, especially to a young woman like you. I want to seduce you and keep you here to live with me.'

She seemed to be mesmerised by the gleam in his eyes. Her own eyes were wide with apprehension. Her heart thumped crazily as she shifted uneasily and lifting the edge of the sheet she pulled it up to hide her bare shoulders from his gaze.

A strange bitter expression chased across his face and he sprang to his feet. Thrusting his hands into the pockets of his well-cut black trousers, he paced away from the bed towards the window. There he turned, a dark shadow against the starlit darkness outside.

'So when did you arrive in Manzanillo?' he demanded curtly.

'Saturday, that was yesterday, and we found out that the Suarez house was further down the coast built on a cliff near a fine beach. Farley and Brett like surfriding too, so they left me at the house and went down to the beach.'

'Didn't Farley want to see your sister after all?' he queried, strolling back towards the bed.

'I asked him to stay with me, but he said it would be best if I were alone when Mr Suarez answered the door.'

'Did Mr Suarez answer the door?'

'No. A man who was some sort of servant did. He said Mr Suarez wasn't at home right then. I asked for Judy, but he shook his head and closed the door in my face. I . . . I . . . guess I was disappointed. I walked back down the drive and found my way to the beach and . . . well, I've told you what happened next.'

'And didn't the kind and helpful Farley try to prevent his friends from throwing you in the sea when he heard you screaming?' he asked with another sarcastic stab at Farley.

'I don't know. I didn't see him when I got down to the beach. There were so many other people. Then I saw Brett....' She covered her eyes with one hand. 'Please don't make me talk about it any more.'

'I have to if we're going to find out whether they intended to let you drown,' he replied quietly, sitting down on the edge of the bed again. 'Don't you see, *chiquita*, no one tried to rescue you. They all left the beach without searching for you. And Farley and Brett must have gone off in the hired car with your clothes and money. How much did you have?'

'Three hundred dollars,' she whispered listlessly.

'In cash?'

'Yes. It was all I had left.'

'And hadn't it ever occurred to you to carry such an amount in the form of traveller's cheques?'

'I did have it in cheques, but Farley said it would be better to cash them before we came.'

'Of course he did.' His irony seared her. 'Cheques which had to be signed by you before they could be cashed would be no good to you and his friend. Your three hundred should keep him going for a few days before he comes across another innocent abroad whom he can live on like the parasite he is. I expect you've paid for every meal he's eaten since he met you, haven't you?'

'Yes,' she admitted miserably. 'But I'm sure he isn't what you say he is. He loved Judy and wanted to find her.'

'Then why didn't he come to this house this afternoon and demand to see Robert Suarez?'

'This house?' she looked at him sharply. 'This is the house I called at? Then you must be....'

'No. I'm not Roberto and I'm not a movie director. I'm Sebastian Suarez and Roberto is my half-brother. His place is nearer to Guadalajara than Manzanillo. He isn't here, nor is your sister. Your friend Farley took you for a ride, *chiquita*, on a wild goose chase.' He glanced at his watch. 'I have to go now—I have a dinner engagement. You're welcome to stay here and recover from your near-drowning. I'll send Manuela to you. She'll look after you.'

'But tomorrow,' she demanded urgently, her glance following his lithe graceful movements as he stood up again. 'What shall I do tomorrow?'

His eyes glimmered at her from between the fringes of thick black lashes as he looked down at her.

'In Mexico we never worry about tomorrow,' he said softly, and touched her cheek again with his forefinger. 'I'll take care of it. Today I saved your life and now it is in my hands. *Buenas noches*.'

He left the room and she stared at the archway through which he had gone, then groaning a little, she twisted on to her side. Had Farley tricked her as Sebastian Suarez had suggested he had? She didn't want to believe Farley was one of those confidence tricksters she had read about and had seen in movies who relied on their wits and their charm to dupe their victims. And what was more, she didn't want to believe she could be duped so easily in spite of the warnings which had been given to her by friends and neighbours when she had set out for Los Angeles to search for her sister.

Where was Judy if she wasn't in this house? What had happened to her if she wasn't living with Robert Suarez? Recalling what had nearly happened to herself that afternoon, she moaned again in horror. She had nearly drowned. If it hadn't been for the enigmatic stranger, Sebastian Suarez, she would now be a corpse, bloated with sea-water, being washed ashore further down the coast.

Farley had known Judy, of that much she was sure. How could he have had a photograph of her in his possession otherwise? Had he beguiled Judy as he had beguiled herself? Had he taken her for a ride down the coast somewhere and let his friends drown her?

Why hadn't he tried to stop his friends from throwing her in the sea? Had he been too high on some drug to notice what was happening to her? Once again she seemed to feel Brett's hands on her arms, feel his hot breath wafting across her face as he laughed. She clutched her head between her hands and rolled about the bed. Oh God, would she ever be able to forget what had happened to her that afternoon? Would she always be wondering if the same thing had happened to Judy, except that in the case of her sister there had been no dark god of the sea to rescue her....

The whisper of sandals on the tiled floor made her look round. The dark-haired plump woman had returned. Over her arms she was carrying an article of clothing. She came over to the bed and by means of gestures indicated that Dawn should sit up and put on the gown she held.

The nightgown, a confection of oyster-coloured silk and beige lace, slipped over Dawn's head with a rustle and clung to her slim body. Looking down at it she couldn't help wondering who owned it. Did it belong to the wife of Sebastian Suarez? Or to his mistress? She wished that either she could speak Spanish or that Manuela could speak English, then she could have found out more about the vital eagle-eyed man who had rescued her.

Manuela pulled back the bedclothes. It was an invitation to Dawn to leave the bed. She slid cautiously to her feet and was glad of the support of Manuela's arm. Slowly the woman guided her across the bright mosaic pattern of cool tiles to a doorway and into a luxurious bathroom. In a few minutes Dawn was undressed again and sitting in shoulder-high scented foam in the deep mushroom-pink bath while the stickiness of sea salt which clung to her hair and skin was washed away by Manuela's big competent hands.

After the bath, feeling soothed and deliciously drowsy, Dawn slipped on the nightgown again and returned to the bedroom where Manuela dried her hair with a blow dryer. Then back into the bed, which had been remade, to sit up against plump pillows, to eat a simple yet sustaining meal of soft-boiled egg and toast and to drink refreshing cold milk.

When the meal was finished Manuela took away the tray and came back to remove one of the pillows from behind Dawn's back.

'Buenas noches, señorita,' she murmured.

'Buenas noches y muchas gracias,' Dawn muttered sleepily, trying out a few of the Spanish words she knew, and thought she saw a smile glimmer in Manuela's dark eyes before her own eyelids, weighted with sleep, fluttered down.

She awoke to the sound of birdsong, a sweet and flute-like solo against the booming beat of the surf on the shore and she opened her eyes to see a bright blue sky through the arched window. The fragrance of many blossoms mingled with the salty tang of the sea wafted in through the opening of the window and for a few minutes she lay still savouring the comfort and beauty of the room and wishing that her awakening moments could always be in such surroundings.

'Buenos dias, señorita.' Manuela appeared through the archway almost as if she hadn't gone very far in the night. She was smiling a little this morning and close behind her came the short sturdily built man who had answered the door of the house when Dawn had called the previous afternoon.

'*Buenos dias, Mees Aylwin*,' he said slowly, his broad-featured walnut-coloured face devoid of expression. 'I have come with Manuela to translate for her. I am Carlos Rivera, her husband. We look after this house for Señor Suarez. You understand?'

'*Si*, I understand.' Dawn sat up and nodded a little shyly .

Manuela turned to her husband then and spoke quickly with many gestures. He listened gravely, frowning a little. When she had finished he talked back, obviously arguing. Manuela's eyes flashed and she interrupted him fiercely. He spoke again, sharply, and Manuela rolled her eyes, lifted her ample shoulders in a despairing shrug.

'Manuela would like you to get out of bed and put on clothes she has brought for you,' said Carlos carefully. 'The clothes belong to our daughter.' He paused and glanced at the ceiling as if in search of inspiration. 'You can use them,' he went on slowly. 'Later you have new clothes.'

'Thank you. *Muchas gracias*,' said Dawn. 'It is kind of you to lend them to me. Please thank your daughter.'

'*De nada*. You are welcome,' said Carlos with a shrug. 'You have breakfast soon, on the terrace.'

He gave her another solemn look and left the room. As soon as he had gone Dawn slid out of bed. In the bathroom she washed her face and hands and peered at herself in the mirror. She had more colour this morning and her hair shimmered in waves about her face. Her eyes looked normal too, greenish grey set between long black lashes, and she felt better, a little more like her lively self.

Manuela had brought nylon panties, an underslip and a wide cotton gown made from heavy Mexican cotton. Pale cream in colour, it had wide sleeves and a deep slit at the front of its round neck. Round the edges of the sleeves and on either side of the slit flowers and leaves had been embroidered in vivid colours, scarlet, yellow, violet and green. Dawn pointed to the embroidery, then at Manuela, who smiled and nodded.

'*Esta bonita*. It's pretty,' said Dawn, trying out another of her Spanish phrases, and Manuela's smile widened.

When she was dressed Dawn slipped on the rope-soled espadrilles Manuela offered to her, then followed the woman from the room to find herself on a wide gallery, edged with black wrought iron railings. Looking up, she saw with surprise that set into the ceiling which was immediately under a flat roof were a series of sloping glass panels through which sunlight filtered, lighting the whole of the square hallway.

She followed Manuela along the gallery past arched openings into other rooms and came to a spiral stairway made from wrought iron which led down to the lower floor of the hallway. In the middle of that floor was a big square pool of water, green and translucent, rippling where the sparkling water from a bronze fountain played into it.

The walls of the hallway were painted a cool silvery green and the floor space at both ends and at both sides was furnished with long couches and easy chairs covered in grey velvet, heaped with grey, green and black striped cushions, round glass-topped occasional tables and strange pieces of sculpture. Potted palms and orange trees, flowering azaleas and other shrubs were everywhere giving the impression that the indoors had become outdoors.

Dawn followed Manuela through an archway into a long sitting room. There were more couches covered this time in topaz-coloured velvet, scattered with cushions of black and gold stripes. Elegant silver candelabra and trays gleamed with discreet opulence against dark oak and paintings in bold vivid colours representing the harsh Mexican landscape hung on the walls.

There were three long arched windows. Manuela opened one of them and indicated that Dawn should go out on to the terrace. Stepping out, she found the air warm and moist and was dazzled by bright sunlight slanting across snow-white walls. The same light touched to fire the roses and gladioli massed in flower beds and added brilliance to the purple of bougainvillaea which cascaded from upstairs balconies.

After glancing at the table set in a corner shaded by lazily drooping palms Dawn went to the wall which edged the terrace and looked over it. Seemingly smooth, living up to its name, the Pacific Ocean stretched milky blue to a hazy violet horizon. Below, clear turquoise, it surged and gurgled among dark rocks at the bottom of the cliff.

Daring herself to look, Dawn leaned over the wall and glanced to her left. She could just see the crescent curve of the beach of golden sand shaded by palm trees between which were looped drying fish-nets. Long rollers of surf creamed along the edge of the beach, but there was no one on it, not even a fisherman. Certainly Farley wasn't there looking for her.

Frowning a little, trying to puzzle out why Farley had deserted her and had left her to drown, she turned away and went to sit at the table. At once, as if summoned by an unheard bell, Carlos appeared carrying a tray laden with dishes. He set before her a glass full of orange juice which was embedded in ice cubes set in a silver dish. Then he placed a silver coffee pot, a pretty ceramic cup and saucer decorated with Mexican designs close to her hand.

'You like fresh fruit salad, cereal and cream, *señorita*?' he asked politely, in his stilted English.

'*Si, por favor*,' she replied in her equally stilted Spanish, and he went swiftly towards the house.

To own a house like this which seemed to hang between the blue sky and the blue sea Sebastian Suarez must be very wealthy, thought Dawn, and at once she felt depressed. She had nothing now. All the money she had possessed had been stolen from her yesterday while she had struggled for life in the ocean.

I'll take care of tomorrow for you, Sebastian Suarez had said. *Your life is in my hands*. All very well for him to say that, but she couldn't let him take over responsibility for her just because he had saved her life. Her innate pride and sense of independence wouldn't let her. She had got herself into this mess and it was up to her to get herself out of it.

But how? That was the problem? How could she travel without money? How could she earn money in a country where she couldn't speak the language? And what was she going to do about identification? As far as she knew the only Canadian government representative was in Mexico City, and that was miles away.

Lost in troubled thoughts, she hardly noticed when Carlos took away the empty fruit juice glass and set before her a dish of fruit salad and placed a bowl of cereal and a jug of fresh cream on the side. Only when he poured coffee into the cup did she look up to thank him and ask,

'Where is Señor Suarez?'

'He come soon. You want more to eat?'

'No, thank you. Does Señor Suarez always live here?'

'No, *señorita*. He have another place in Guadalajara. This is *la casa chica*—the little house. Excuse me, *por favor*.'

So this was the *little* house, was it? Dawn's mouth curved wryly as she dipped a spoon into the fruit salad. If this house was to be considered *little* a big house must be like a palace!

For the next few moments she forgot about her problems as she enjoyed the delicious fruits; dices of juicy melon, segments of grapefruit and avocado pear, decorated with tiny sweet strawberries. Then she turned to the cereal. It was crisp and crunchy and the cream was smooth and rich.

It was while she was sipping her last cup of coffee that she felt she was being watched. Looking across at the house, she saw Sebastian Suarez standing at one of the long windows, hands in the pockets of his trousers. When he realised she had seen him he stepped on to the terrace and strolled across to her. Dark glasses covered his eyes, but when he reached the table he removed them, dangling them from his fingers.

'*Buenos dias*, Dawn. Have you breakfasted well?' he asked.

'Yes, thank you.' She felt suddenly extremely breathless. Her heartbeats had increased at the most alarming rate and she could actually feel her cheeks growing hot. And what was even more alarming, she didn't seem able to stop staring at him in the same way that he was staring at her. Both of them were studying each other as if to make sure their eyes hadn't been deceived by what they had seen the previous night.

She had missed a few details about him, she thought. She hadn't noticed the few streaks of silver hairs among the black close to his temples. Nor had she realised how deeply the lines of humour about his mouth and eyes had been carved. He was wearing a leisure shirt made from black knitted cotton. It was collarless and short-sleeved. Its deep slit opening at the front was carelessly laced together by a white cord. Its close fit emphasised the muscularity of his shoulders, chest and arms.

His powerful physical magnetism packed a punch which struck her somewhere below the ribs so that she felt even more breathless and shaky. With an effort she looked away from him, down at the table, and fiddled nervously with the spoon in the cereal dish, and the spell which had held them silent and motionless for a whole minute was broken.

He spun the other chair round and straddled it. He tossed his sun-glasses on the table and folded his brawny hair-flecked forearms along the top of the back of the chair.

'Forgive me for staring at you. It was rude of me,' he surprised her by saying. 'But you see I had doubts all last night about your existence.' His mouth curved in a grin of self-derision. 'Usually I'm not given to fantasy-making and it's a great relief to know that I haven't imagined you and all that happened yesterday afternoon and evening and that you are really here. So, how do you feel today? Better, hmmm?'

'Yes, thank you,' she said again, stiffly and primly, keeping her glance on the silver spoon.

'Carlos and Manuela have treated you well?' he asked, and there was a certain sharpness in his voice.

'Oh, yes, of course they have,' she answered quickly. It wouldn't do for him to think that his employees hadn't done their best for her.

'Then what is the matter?' he rapped.

'Nothing.' She looked up, her eyes wide.

'No?' The glint in his eyes and the twist to his mouth were sardonic. 'Is this the way you usually are, then, in the morning? Stiff and prickly like a little porcupine which senses danger. Ha!' His laugh was short and like his grin had been, self-mocking. 'Perhaps my imagination did run riot last night, for I had the impression of some-one quite different, of someone warm and natural who didn't hesitate to show her feelings, of someone who would love deeply when she fell in love and never count the cost.'

His voice had deepened to a caressing murmur and again she felt breathless. Cheeks aflame, she looked down again. The spoon tinkled against the cup as she fiddled with it. Then suddenly her hand was engulfed by a larger sinewy hand, deeply tanned and flecked with hairs, and the spoon dropped from her nerveless fingers. From under her lashes she gave him a slow glance which seemed to amuse him, for he grinned, his teeth flashing white.

'So you give me a look which says go to hell just be-cause I take your hand in mine, *chiquita*.' His fingers tightened remorselessly on her hand while his thumb caressed the thin skin inside her wrist so that a tingling sensation ran up the nerves of her arm and seemed to spread through her whole body like a shock. 'But you see,' he went on softly, 'I don't like it when you prefer playing with a spoon to looking at me, and I don't like being spoken to in that cold stand-offish way as if I'm of no account to you.'

Across the table above their entwined hands their eyes met and clashed, and Dawn had the craziest feeling she was locked in a duel with him to prove who had the superior strength. Looking at him, thinking of the little she knew about him, there was no doubt in her mind that he regarded himself as superior to her, for the simple reason that he was male. A fully mature man in superb physical condition and, Mexican into the bargain, he was probably as adept at singing and playing a serenade to his lady-love as he was at riding the surf or performing other athletic feats or at defending his honour. He was pure *macho* and obviously used to getting his own way.

But his attitude, the way he was holding her hand as if he had a right to do so and the way he had rebuked her brought her fighting Irish blood to the boil. She longed to hurl his words back in his face to tell him he wasn't of any account to her—and then she remembered he had saved her life the day before. *She owed him her life.* The thought was disturbing and it had the effect of putting the lid on her simmering temper for the time being.

'I can't see anything wrong in the way I spoke to you,' she argued. 'I answered your questions politely.'

'So politely that I feel frozen,' he retorted with a quirk of humour. 'A blast of icy wind from the Arctic regions.'

'Oh!' she exclaimed. 'I didn't mean to be like that. Please try to understand. I'm still feeling confused and a little nervous. I realise I'm under an obligation to you for rescuing me yesterday, but....'

'There is a way in which you could pay that obligation very easily,' he interrupted her.

'How? Please tell me,' she demanded impulsively.

'All you have to do is stay here for a while,' he replied, and again his thumb caressed her wrist and she felt the delicious sensuous tingle shiver along her nerves. Puzzled by his suggestion as well as a little alarmed by the effect his touch was having on her, she gave him another wary glance and took fright at the expression in his clear golden eyes. He was watching her as an eagle would watch its prey, coldly, objectively ready to swoop down and take it.

She was on her feet in an instant, determined to leave, find her way through the house and through its surrounding grounds to the road, be on her way. Where she would go she wasn't quite sure at that moment, but the instinct to run away from this powerful, attractive man before he could take over her life and run it for her was strong.

Yet he was still holding her hand and she couldn't get it free no matter how hard she tried. Her breasts heaving under the loose-fitting cotton gown, her eyes smoky with hatred, she glared down at him, too angry to speak.

'Now, you remind me of a bird,' he drawled, rising to his feet and standing before her still holding her hand in his, coming so close to her that their two hands held at the level of his chest were all that separated them. 'You remind me of a pretty parakeet I found once in the forest when I was a boy. It had a broken wing, so I took it home with me, intending to mend the wing. I put the bird in a cage and for a while it was most unhappy. It kept trying to escape, banging against the bars and hurting itself.'

'Wh-what happened to it?' she asked, fascinated by his story in spite of herself.

'It got used to the cage and to me. We became great friends. It grew so tame I was able to let it out for a few hours every day knowing it would always return to me.' He raised his free hand and touched her jaw-line close to her ear with gentle finger-tips in a feather-light caress which seemed to turn her knees to water. 'I wouldn't like you to get hurt, *chiquita*, trying to get away from me.'

There was a tense breathless moment as she stared at him and absorbed the message of his little story. Then her temper boiled over.

'I am not a bird, *señor*,' she retorted, jerking her head back from those seductive fingers of his. 'I am a free woman, and you mustn't think that you have to look after me just because you saved my life. I'm very grateful to you, truly I am, but I can't stay here. I must go.'

'Go where?' he queried, letting go of her hand and folding his arms across his chest, but even though he had released her she guessed she hadn't a hope of getting past him. He would just reach out and grab her, and she wasn't going to give him the chance to lay hands on her.

'To Manzanillo, I suppose,' she said coolly, her head high. 'It's the nearest town.'

'You intend to go dressed like that?' His gaze roved critically over the cotton gown. 'On foot?' He shook his head slowly from side to side. '*Por dios*, that would be foolish. You wouldn't get very far walking in the heat. It's almost noon and your white skin would blister and burn. You would get sunstroke. And supposing you did reach Manzanillo, what would you do there? You haven't any money or identification.' His mouth took on a straight determined line. 'No, I can't let you go, *señorita*. If anything happened to you on the way or in Manzanillo I would never forgive myself.'

'What could possibly happen?' she demanded, trying to hide the dismay she was feeling, knowing he was quite right and she would have problems explaining to any authority in Manzanillo why she was in the country. 'I'm quite capable of looking after myself.'

'Are you?' His eyebrows tilted mockingly. 'I don't believe you are. Look what happened to you yesterday.'

The sound of footsteps coming across the terrace made them both look round. Carlos was coming, swinging his tray in his hand. When he reached them he spoke to Sebastian quickly in Spanish. Sebastian nodded and answered, then turned to Dawn.

'Excuse me, *por favor*,' he said. 'I have to go and speak with a police officer who has come to the house. Please stay here on the terrace. It might be necessary for you to talk to him too.'

'Why?' she exclaimed.

'I decided to report the theft of the hired car to the police. I've told them you're my guest—I thought if I arranged it that way it would give you a certain amount of protection.'

And would put her more than ever under an obligation to him, she thought, give him more of a hold over her.

'It wasn't necessary to report it as a theft,' she said coldly.

'I think it was,' he retorted. 'You hired it and it was taken from you.' His mouth curled sardonically. 'I believe in facing facts, *señorita*. It has been stolen from you. Now hold yourself in readiness to be interviewed. The police sergeant will want to know the make, the colour and the year of the car, also the name of the rental agency in Los Angeles so that the Green Fleet, as we call our highway patrol, can be on the look-out for it. And remember, the sooner it is found the sooner you will have your money and your clothes back and you'll be as free as a wild bird again. Unless,' he added dryly, 'your kind and helpful friend Farley has disposed of them already.'

He turned away and went into the house. Dawn stood beside the table, staring after him and biting her lip. She could go now if she wanted to. She could go down the steps she had seen winding through the thick vegetation of primavera, papayas and palms which grew on the slopes of the cliff, down to the public beach. Once there it was possible she would find someone who could give her a lift in a car to Manzanillo.

But what good would running away do now? It would only be a gesture of defiance thrown in the face of the autocratic Sebastian Suarez and it would achieve nothing. Common sense dictated that she would be better off waiting here under his protection until there was news of the hired car. The police were much more likely to act for him, a Mexican national, than they were for her, a stranger without any form of identification.

Sighing a little because it went against the grain to have to give in to male authority, she turned to Carlos, who had almost finished clearing the table.

'Does anyone else live here besides Señor Suarez?' she asked.

'Manuela, me and our daughter,' he replied woodenly.

'I realised that,' she said with a touch of impatience.' I mean does Señor Suarez have a wife and children?'

Carlos lifted the tray and balanced it cleverly on one hand close to his shoulder. His black slanted eyes regarded her with cool indifference.

'He does not have a wife, *señorita*,' he replied politely. 'I do not know if he has any children or not. Excuse me, *por favor*.'

He went off in his brisk fashion and, feeling a little as if he had brushed her off as he might brush off a persistent mosquito which kept nibbling at him, Dawn wandered over to the wall and looked down at the green-blue water swirling among the rocks. The heat of the sun beat down on her bare head, the back of her neck, and Carlos's last few enigmatic words went round and round in her mind.

I do not know if he has any children or not—meaning that Sebastian Suarez could have fathered children but that Carlos didn't consider it any of her business if he had. The message was loud and clear: Carlos wasn't prepared to tell her anything about his employer.

How then was she going to find out about the man who had plucked her from the sea and had brought her into his house? Elbows on the rough stone of the wall, chin on her hands, she watched the water leaping in a cascade of glittering drops against dark jagged rocks, throwing up tiny pebbles and pieces of driftwood and leaving them stranded there. Like one of those pebbles or a piece of that driftwood she had been washed up on the edge of Sebastian Suarez's life, so why should she think it was important to know more about him?

'Señorita?' Carlos was back on the terrace and calling to her. She turned to look at him and immediately had to shade her eyes against the sun-dazzled, snow-white complex of the house. 'Will you come, por favor, to the salon?' Carlos asked.

CHAPTER TWO

THE young policeman, Sergeant Diego Moreles of the Green Fleet highway patrol, spoke English well and treated her with gentle yet firm courtesy. When she gave him details of the rented car he wrote down the information in a notebook, sitting beside her on one of the long velvet-covered couches while Sebastian Suarez stood at a nearby window, seemingly not a part of the interview yet obviously listening to everything that was being said.

'And you believe this car was stolen from you, señorita?' asked the policeman when he had finished writing.

'No, not stolen, just borrowed,' she replied firmly, and was aware that Sebastian Suarez turned sharply away from the window. In a few strides he was across the room and standing beside her.

'But Señor Suarez reported a theft,' exclaimed the sergeant.

'I know, but I don't believe it was stolen deliberately,' said Dawn earnestly. 'You see, I came down here in the company of two young men from Los Angeles and they have driven off in the car somewhere and I don't know where they've gone. I'd be grateful if you could find them, because in the car is my purse, my passport and tourist card and my clothes.'

'The young men were hitch-hikers, perhaps?' said the policeman writing busily in his notebook.

'No. We had arranged to travel together. One of them is a friend of my sister and I don't want him to be arrested for theft if you find him with the car. I'm sure he's only borrowed it for a while.'

The policeman was obviously puzzled and he glanced up at Sebastian Suarez as if expecting some sort of guidance.

'Your heart is too soft, Dawn, *querida*,' said Sebastian, a note of indulgent amusement in his voice, and Dawn couldn't help giving him an upward glance of surprise at his use of the endearment. At once his eyes flashed a warning at her and he put a hand on her shoulder to press it. 'She finds it difficult to believe badly of anyone, Sergeant,' he added, looking at the policeman.

'*Si*, I understand,' replied the sergeant, his frown of puzzlement clearing. 'Then perhaps you could give me a description of your friends, *señorita*, and also their names. It will make it easier for us to approach them if we should find the car.'

Dawn described Farley and Brett as well as she could and gave their full names, and the policeman took more notes.

'Have you any idea in which direction they would go?' he asked. 'Would they turn inland and make for Mexico City? Or would they aim for Acapulco?'

'They like surf-riding, so I think they would keep to the coast,' she said.

'*Bueno*, then we shall do our best to trace them for you,' said the sergeant, putting his notebook away and rising to his feet. 'The patrol truck drivers in the area will be given all these details and asked to keep a look-out during the next few days. I'll report back as soon as I have some information for you. You'll be staying here, of course?'

His dark eyes were glinting with sudden interest as their glance lingered on the soft sheen of her pale hair. No longer was he an impersonal public servant doing his duty but a lively young man who liked young women and was possibly wondering at her presence in that house. And now by asking that question he had trapped her into making a commitment which she had been trying to avoid. She hesitated, wondering how to answer, and felt Sebastian's hand press her shoulder warningly again. It was no use, she would have to say she was going to stay there for the next few days. It was the only way she would get news of the car and of Farley. Without the support of Sebastian Suarez the police were going to be very suspicious of her.

'Yes, I'll be staying here,' she murmured, and felt the pressure of Sebastian's hand again before he withdrew it.

'That is good.' The sergeant's smile flashed white beneath the darkness of his moustache and his eyes glowed with admiration. 'Then I wish you good day, *señorita*.'

'*Buenos dias*, and thank you,' she replied.

'*De nada*. It has been a great pleasure meeting you.'

He left somewhat reluctantly, urged on his way by Sebastian. Alone, Dawn leaned back against the plump velvet cushions of the divan and gave a sigh of relief. She was glad the questioning was over and that the policeman had been sympathetic and that she had been able to put in a word for Farley which would prevent him from being arrested for theft if he was found with the car. She knew that Sebastian hadn't been pleased because what she had told the policeman was in direct contradiction with what he had told him, but she couldn't help that. She was sure Farley wasn't a thief. At least she wasn't sure, but she hoped he wasn't.

And now she was committed to staying here for a few days whether she wanted to stay or not; committed to staying with the enigmatic, forceful Sebastian Suarez in this luxurious, exotic house all green and gold inside, open and airy with rounded arches and wrought iron screens instead of doors.

If only she knew more about him or could find out more about him she would feel better about staying with him. She realised by the way the policeman had behaved that he commanded respect, but that could be merely because he was wealthy and not because his character was good. And there were all sorts of unpleasant ways by which a person as young as he was could become wealthy these days. He could be involved in drug-peddling or white-slave traffic.

Smiling a little at the way her imagination was running wild, Dawn looked round the room in search of something which might give her a clue to Sebastian's background. In a small alcove partially cut off from the rest of the room by a wrought iron screen there was a dainty escritoire, an antique writing table made from gleaming walnut wood, on which a group of framed photographs were arranged.

Getting to her feet, she went over to the alcove and sat down in the elegant chair which was placed in front of it. The three photographs all seemed to be of the same person, a woman. Two of them were studio portraits, close-ups of a heart-shaped face framed by waves of dark hair. Long-lashed eyes looked out directly and with a glint of mockery that was familiar. The other photograph was of the same woman sitting with a silver-haired man on a garden seat in front of the house.

'I am glad to see you are making yourself at home.'

Sebastian's voice made her start guiltily and she tried to put the photograph she was holding back in its place. But she was clumsy and knocked down the outer two photographs. One of them skidded along the top of the table and fell to the floor. At once she jumped out of the chair and bent to pick up the fallen picture, only to find that he had moved to pick it up too and that their hands reached for it at the same time. Quickly she withdrew her hand and straightened up.

'I'm sorry,' she said stiffly. 'I didn't mean to knock them down.'

'*No importa*,' he murmured with a shrug, and re-arranged the photographs.

'She is very beautiful,' she remarked, hoping to find out who the woman was.

'*Sí*. Many people have told me that. I don't remember her myself. She died when I was two,' he replied coolly, turning to look at her, and at once she knew why the eyes of the woman in the photograph were familiar. They were like his. 'My father, whom you can see sitting there with her, built this house for her. She called it her "gilded cage".' Again he shrugged. 'I don't know why.'

His remarks made something go click in her mind and her memory began to whirr like a movie film. A gilded cage. The phrase was familiar. Why? Her glance went again to the photographs of the man and woman. The man was easily more than twenty years older than the woman, old enough to be her father.

'The house is lovely,' she said, 'and from the outside it looks like something straight out of the Arabian Nights with all those Moorish arches and domes.'

'You have read the stories from the Arabian Nights?' he asked, his eyebrows lifting in surprise.

'Yes, many times. My father had a copy which had belonged to his mother. It had wonderful exotic pictures. Judy and I read it so often that I'm afraid we wore it out and it fell to pieces.'

'There is a copy of it here,' he said, reaching a hand to the shelves above the desk on which there were a few books and some small ornaments. He took down a slim volume bound in green with gilt lettering and held it out to her. 'It belonged to her and perhaps it was from one of the pictures that she got the idea of how she would like the house to be designed.'

Dawn took the book from him. It was very similar to the one her father had owned and on the fly-leaf the name of the owner was written in flowing cursive writing. Polly Moore. *Polly Moore*. It sounded Irish and vaguely familiar, like the name of someone her father might have known, someone in show business.

'It could be,' she said in agreement with him, glancing at one of the pictures. 'But this house is much too big to be called the little house.'

'*Como dice?*' He sounded puzzled. 'What is it you are saying?'

'*La casa chica*,' she said slowly and carefully. 'I think
that is how you say it and it means little house. That is
what Carlos told me this house is called when I asked him
if you lived here all the time. He said you have another
house and this is just *la casa chica*. Oh, what have I said?
Why are you laughing?'

'I laugh because only an innocent stranger to Mexico
would misunderstand,' he replied. The laughter faded
from his face and his mouth twisted wryly. 'There is another meaning to *casa chica*.'

'What is it?'

'I'm not sure I should tell you,' he replied with a glint
of mockery in his eyes.

'Oh, why not?'

'Because I believe that where you come from such
places rarely exist and you might be shocked.'

'I'd still like to know, then I won't make a mistake
again.'

'Okay.' He shrugged again. 'The little house is a way of
referring to the extra-marital establishment for the husband's pleasure, the place in fact where his mistress lives
separate from the house where his wife and family live.
Me entiende Usted? You understand me?'

Dawn nodded, feeling her cheeks grow warm. She
handed the book back to him and when he turned away
to put it on the shelf she looked again at the photographs.
Had he just implied that his mother had been his father's
mistress?

'And what else did you learn from Carlos?' He spoke
sharply as he turned and stepped towards her. The cold-
ness of his voice and the hard, critical expression in his
eyes warned her that he wasn't pleased that she had
questioned his houseman.

'Not much. He's very close-mouthed,' she replied.

'I should hope he is. I don't employ him to gossip about me to my guests.'

'I didn't want him to gossip about you,' she retorted with a defiant lift of her chin.

'Then why ask him questions about me?'

'I was only trying to find out a few facts about you. After all, you questioned me last night and found out all about me. All I know about you is your name. I can guess you're wealthy by the style in which you live.' Her glance flicked round the beautiful room and came back to him.

'Why do you want to know more?' he demanded. 'So that you can decide if I'm to be trusted, right?' His mouth curved bitterly and his eyes sparkled angrily. 'What a pity you didn't think to check up on Farley before deciding to trust him,' he sneered. 'If you had you wouldn't have been thrown into the ocean yesterday and left to drown, would you? You wouldn't have been rescued by me and have to stay here dependent on my goodwill and support.' He stepped closer to her, bending his head so that her startled eyes could see nothing but his face with the golden eyes brightly menacing. 'But I am flattered by your own interest,' he drawled, 'and it's going to give me great pleasure to show you, pretty bird, just how interested I am in you.'

His intention was clear to her now. He was going to kiss her. He was assuming she would let him kiss her. But no man, not even this one to whom she owed her life, was going to kiss her against her will. She stepped backwards and collided with the wrought iron screen which was behind her. She was off balance for a moment and he reached out a hand to steady her, grasping the bodice of the gown she was wearing and holding it at the slit opening, and looking down at his hand she had a wild feeling that whatever it caught and held would never escape.

'I'm all right,' she assured him. 'You can let go now.' Her voice was as sharp as an icicle, her head held high as she looked him in the eyes, but she felt her heart fluttering in her breast like a captured bird.

'In a little while,' he murmured, and drew her towards him by pulling on the stuff of the gown.

'No! Let go now. You're not going to kiss me. I won't let you,' she cried, and her hand swung up to strike at him. But her blow never landed because he caught her wrist and then somehow instead of being free as she had hoped she was in his arms, was close against him so that she could feel the hard bones and muscles of his body thrusting against the softness of hers through the thin cotton clothing they were both wearing, and the intimacy of that contact sent waves of shock reverberating through her.

In outrage she flung her head back, turning her face sideways to him and arching her body away from him back over his arms, but there was no way she could avoid the touch of his lips against the long curve of her throat.

The feel of that bold predatory mouth against her tender skin sent her crazy for a few moments. Writhing in the trap he had made with his arms, uttering little cries of protest and sheer panic, her soft fine hair flying out in all directions as she shook her head, and her sandalled feet kicking futilely against his hard legs, she struggled to escape until with an impatient exclamation in Spanish he caught and held her face captive with one hand. For a moment their eyes met, hers shimmering with hate, his blazing with anger, then his mouth took hers in a hard punishing kiss.

That insidious tingle which had sparked along her

nerves when he had stroked her wrist flashed through her now, a warning that he was dangerous to her in an embrace as close as this was. Her brain dictated she should fight to break free of him, but her senses ignored the order, because suddenly the quality of his kiss changed. His lips softened and parted, stroking hers gently, tempting them to respond, and slowly hers softened too and opened. Her eyes closed and all conscious thought was wiped out by new and pleasant sensations.

Long ripples of sensuousness flowed through her as she lost the desire to fight. Her body became pliable and moulded itself eagerly against his as a new need grew within her, a sort of ache for something, she wasn't quite sure what; something like a joy which was beyond kissing and which she might be able to reach if she stayed with him.

His lips left hers and at once she came whirling down from somewhere near heaven and plummeted back to earth. She opened her eyes to see him looking down at her, his parted lips curving in a faintly mocking smile, his eyes glinting at her from between half-closed lashes. Still holding her with one arm, he ran an exploratory finger round the inside of the neckline of her gown and his touch sent a shiver down her spine. Then his finger tip trailed insinuatingly against her skin inside the slit opening and she caught her breath in a wild gasp. Lifting a hand, she grasped his hand to stop his piratical finger from marauding further. Immediately his hand turned under hers. His fingers curved about hers and in a graceful courtly gesture he raised her hand to his lips and kissed the back of it, all the time watching her with those glinting mocking eyes.

'So now you know a little more about me, *chiquita*,' he said softly. 'And I know something about you, and I am glad you have agreed to stay.'

'I'm only staying because the sergeant of police said he would bring the information about the car and my belongings here,' she retorted, snatching her hand from his and stepping back against the screen again. 'I'm not staying here to oblige you.'

'Yet your staying will oblige me,' he replied, his glance flicking over her provocatively. 'After all, I am my father's son and like him I enjoy having a pretty companion to share this *casa chica* of his with me.'

'Oh, you're assuming too much, far too much,' she gasped furiously.

'I am? In what way?'

'You're assuming that I would like to be your companion. Well, you're wrong.' She flung out an arm and pointed to the photographs on the writing table. 'I don't want to be like her,' she added. 'I don't want to be a bird in a gilded cage, sold for an old man's gold!'

There was an unpleasant little silence. Something wicked came and went in his clear eyes and she remembered belatedly that he was Mexican and might consider an insult to his mother an insult to his honour and find a cruel way to retaliate. But to her surprise he shrugged and his mouth took on a humorous curve.

'I don't consider myself to be old, yet, perhaps twelve years older than you are, in the prime of life, as they say,' he said. The humour faded and was replaced by a frown of puzzlement. 'But I don't understand the reference to being sold for gold. Would you care to explain?'

Her tongue came out to lick her throbbing lips which were suddenly dry and she watched him warily.

'It ... it's an old music hall song,' she muttered. 'I remembered it when you said your mother called this house a gilded cage. My father used to sing the song sometimes.'

'He did? Why? Was he a singer?'

'Yes, and an actor. He used to sing in musical plays and he was also a regular performer in a T.V. series in Canada, a sort of sing-along show. It was in that show that I heard him sing the song.'

'Tell me more about the song, *por favor*,' he urged.

'It's about a young woman who has married an old man for his money. One line goes like this: "Her beauty sold for an old man's gold, she's a bird in a gilded cage." ' Dawn sang the words in her husky contralto voice. 'Haven't you ever heard it before?'

'No, but you have just explained something which has puzzled me for years. I'll show you.' He stepped over to the writing table, opened its drawer and took out a book bound in real leather. 'This is my mother's diary,' he said, turning back to her. 'She used to sit at this table, so I'm told. She was a singer too and a dancer and appeared in several Hollywood films. My father provided the financial backing for them. He made a lot of money that way.' He opened the book at the first page and handed it to her. 'Please read it,' he invited.

Dawn took the book from him and looked down at the sloping writing which covered the page. She read:

'Today is my first day in this house, this lovely gilded cage which Clemente has built for me. I sang that song to him about the bird in the gilded cage. I thought he would laugh, but he didn't. He was very upset and told me he doesn't want me to think of myself or him in that way. He says it hurts him because he can't marry me. He says I'm much more his wife than Raquel has ever been. Theirs was one of those arranged marriages and not a love affair. They haven't lived together for years. My poor Clemente, for all his wealth he hasn't had much happiness in his life. I must try to make him happy while I can. I love him so much.'

Dawn closed the book and stood looking down at it. Sebastian's retaliation for what she had implied about his mother was very subtle, she thought, and it hurt her far more than any show of anger would have done.

'I'm sorry for what I said,' she said simply, handing the book back to him. 'I see now that I was wrong.'

'Yet if you hadn't said what you did I wouldn't have found out why my father was upset by the song,' he replied, putting the book back in the drawer. 'He didn't have to buy her beauty or her companionship. She loved him and gave up everything to come and live with him, her career and her friends and her family who frowned on her association with him. It was his greatest regret that after being together nearly six years she lived only a year after they were married.' He noticed her upward glance of surprise and his mouth twisted wryly. '*Si*, they were married eventually, soon after I was born. His first wife agreed to divorce him when she learned I was expected.'

'Why have you told me all this?' she asked.

'Partly because you wanted to know more about me and I would rather tell you myself than have you learn about it secondhand and partly to clear up a misconception you had of my mother, a prejudice which might have prevented the growth of our relationship.'

'But we don't have a relationship,' she objected.

'I can't agree with you,' he retorted. 'We do, and it keeps changing. Last night it was between the rescuer—me and the rescued one—you. This morning it has been the protector—me and the protected one—you while you were interviewed by the sergeant of police. And now it's. . . .'

'Between predator and prey,' she put in quickly.

'*No entiendo*,' he said, his eyebrows coming together in a puzzled frown. 'I don't understand.'

'You like to be in the position of superiority, don't you?' she taunted. 'Rescuer, protector and now predator, and I am the prey. Because I'm trapped here in your house you think you have the right to make love to me any time you want whether I want to or not. You ... you're so *macho* you make me feel sick!'

His face went taut and pale almost as if she had struck him and his eyes blazed with an unholy light. For a moment she felt her legs shake, but she didn't retreat. She faced up to him, defying him. Then his eyelids dropped over his eyes and a mocking smile slanted his mouth which had the effect of making her feel more apprehensive than ever.

'Brave words,' he jeered. 'But I don't believe them. You've just shown me you're not averse to making love. When I kissed you.... *Dios*, what is the matter now?' His voice rose sharply.

Greatly disturbed because he had noticed the way she had responded to his kiss, Dawn had hidden her hot face in her hands.

'How unfair you are, how despicable!' she raged in a fierce whisper. 'First you try to kiss me against my will....'

'I only wanted to show you I like the way you look,' he interrupted her angrily.

'Couldn't you have told me? Did you have to kiss me?' she flared, lowering her hands and glaring at him.

'*Si*, I did,' he replied. 'I come from a passionate warm-blooded people who show their feelings without reservation, who hug and kiss one another regardless of sex. How was I to know you'd behave like a hellcat when I touched you, kicking me, blinding me and nearly choking me with your hair, behaving as if you believed I was going to rape you?'

'Then why didn't you let go of me when I showed you I didn't want to be kissed? Why did you persist?' she countered.

He took a short hissing breath and threw up his hands in a gesture of helplessness.

'I couldn't help myself,' he groaned. 'Hasn't anyone ever told you that a sure-fire way of rousing a man's passion is to resist him as you resisted me?'

'You kissed me by force,' she declared. 'And then when I seemed to respond you assumed I like being kissed by you.'

'So you *seemed* to respond? Ha!' His crack of laughter made her flinch. 'Oh no, you didn't *seem* to respond,' he taunted softly. 'You did. That was no pretence, and naturally I assumed you liked it. And I'm willing to bet that the next time it happens you'll respond even more.'

'There won't be a next time,' she stormed at him. 'Do you really believe I'll stay here knowing you're the sort of man who insists on forcing your attentions on innocent women who don't want them?'

There was another ominous silence while he glared at her, his eyes bright with anger, his finely chiselled nostrils flaring as he breathed heavily in an effort to control himself. Then as if he didn't trust them he thrust his hands into his pockets and paced away from her slowly, only to swing round suddenly and come towards her again.

'All right, I admit it,' he said in a low voice. 'I admit I want you. I'm attracted to you and I'd like to make love to you any time I feel like it. But not if you're unwilling. There's no pleasure in taking an unwilling woman and I've never gone in for that sort of thing, no matter what you think.' He paused and his glance flicked over her.

'And I don't believe you didn't like being kissed by me. So you can get on with your despising. I care that much.' He snapped his finger and thumb together. 'And now I must go to work.'

'To work?' she exclaimed.

'Ah, you are surprised now that I work? You believe me to be a playboy, hmm?' Again his eyes glinted angrily. '*Por dios*, you ought to be punished in some way for your ignorant prejudices, *señorita*. *Si*, I am going to work to the meeting in Guadalajara of a committee of which I am a member. It is to do with the government of this state.' He turned away and stepped out of the alcove.

'Is Guadalajara a long way from here?' she asked as she followed him.

'It'll take me about an hour to fly there in my Cessna.'

'You fly your own plane?'

'*Si*. Flying and sky-diving are my greatest pleasures,' he replied coolly, and paused in his stride to look back at her. 'Anything else you would like to know about me before I go?' he added with an ironic curve to his mouth, and she could only shake her head. 'Then I'll be on my way. Please use the house as if it were your own home while you wait for the sergeant to bring you news. I'll be back maybe this evening, maybe tomorrow.'

He strode on to the archway and she watched him go feeling a strange desire to stop him from going surge up inside her.

'I might not be here when you come back,' she called after him in an attempt to draw his attention back to her, and once again he turned to face her, although he continued on his way, walking backwards towards the archway.

'So if you're not here, you're not here,' he retorted with a mocking smile and a shrug of his shoulders. He placed the tips of the fingers of one hand to his lips and kissed them to her. '*Adios*, pretty bird, *hasta la vista*.'

He strode out of the room and she heard him calling to Carlos in the hallway. Then all was quiet. For a while Dawn stood rubbing her lips with her fingers as if she could rub out the impression he had made on them. Her emotions were still boiling and bubbling as a result of what had happened between herself and Sebastian and she tried to figure out who had come out of it best. Surely she had. He had left the house and she was free to go. And yet. . . .

Irritated by the way he had disturbed her, she wiped the back of her hands across her mouth. A man had kissed her. So what? She had been kissed before by young men who had taken her out for an evening and she had let them kiss her, wanting to find out what it was like, wanting to know if she would feel any exciting sensations as a result. But she had never felt anything and had come to the conclusion that all she had read about sexual love was a lot of rubbish. She had never felt any desire to be closer to a man until just now when Sebastian had kissed her.

And if he hadn't stopped kissing her, if he had continued to hold and caress her what would have happened? The nerves in the pit of her stomach fluttered and a tingling sensuousness flowed through her as her imagination ran wild. She swayed where she stood, then clutched at her head with her hands. What was the matter with her? *The next time it happens you'll respond even more*. His mocking words taunted her. He was right, she would. So she must leave while he was away. She would go now, this very minute.

She went into the hallway. Its cool airiness was enhanced by the tinkle of the fountain, by the clever use of wrought iron and the diffused light slanting in from the ceiling, and more than ever she had the impression that the whole house was a beautiful cage from which she must escape before she was tempted into staying in it for ever.

She opened the front door and stepped outside. The heat hit her like a blast from a furnace and she nearly retreated into the coolness of the hall. Then she heard the high-toned drone of the engine of a light plane and went down the steps to the driveway. Looking up, she shaded her eyes with a hand against the brilliant sunlight. A small blue and white plane which had just taken off nearby zoomed over her and swooped off in the direction of the misty purple mountains which she could see soaring against the blue sky beyond the fringe of palm trees which marked the boundary of the land surrounding the house.

She watched the plane until it was only a twinkle of light in the hot hazy sky, aware of a longing to be in it, sitting beside its pilot as it swooped higher and higher to cleave its way through a gorge between the mountains. Then the twinkle was swallowed up in the heat haze and even though she stared hard she couldn't see it any longer.

Her hand dropped to her side and she felt a strange sense of having been abandoned, left behind. Resentful of the feeling, she shook it off and stepped into the shade provided by the line of palm trees on one side of the driveway and began to walk away from the house. She would walk down to the road. Perhaps she might be able to thumb a lift into Manzanillo. Once there she would go to the police station and ask if the police would help her to get in touch with the Canadian Embassy.

Ahead of her heat waves shimmered above the hard

bright surface of the path. It was noon, not the best time to go walking in this climate. Even yesterday at four o'clock it had been very hot when she had walked down this driveway. Then she had been wearing a wide-brimmed Mexican straw hat to protect her head and neck and shade her eyes. She had worn tough canvas rubber-soled tennis shoes. Yet still she had suffered from sunburn on the tops of her arms which had been left bare by the sleeveless cotton T-shirt she had been wearing with her jeans.

Now her arms and shoulder tips were covered by the sleeves of the cotton gown. But she had no hat and her neck was bare. The sandals she was wearing were no protection against the rough stones of the road.

So much had happened to her since yesterday afternoon when, disappointed because she hadn't found Judy, she had trudged down this driveway to look for Farley and tell him. She felt like a different person. Yesterday she had been so sure Farley would come up with another idea on how to approach Robert Suarez. Now she was confused and not really sure that what she was intending to do next was right.

But she couldn't stay in that beautiful gilded cage of a house and wait. She was afraid that if she stayed she would never want to leave. She was afraid of the man who owned it and to whom she owed her life. She was afraid of what had happened to her when he had taken her in his arms. Instinctively she guessed he could show her what heaven was like, but once he had shown her what then? She wasn't so naïve that she could believe they would live happily ever afterwards.

And anyway she had still to find Judy, had still to carry out her father's dying wish that his eldest daughter, the one who was so like him and who had followed in his footsteps to be an entertainer, should be found and be told of the small amount of money he had left to her in his will. Dawn's lips twisted into a wry smile. She had spent her own small amount on flying out to L.A. and what was left of it had been in her purse and for all she knew could have been spent by now.

She was coming to the end of the driveway, thank goodness, and already she was limping. Before swinging open one of the big wrought iron gates she stopped and with her finger eased out a small pebble which had become caught between the rope sole of the sandal and the bottom of her left foot. Then she wiped the sweat from her brow on the back of one hand. For a moment she stared through the delicate black tracery of ironwork and looked out at the road. Bare and dusty, it stretched away towards the mountains, edged on either side with swampy-looking land, and she remembered with a slight sinking of her spirits that the peninsula of land on which the Suarez house and several other luxurious hideaways were built was a dead end. To reach the north-south highway linking the coastal towns she would have to walk about three miles.

Taking a deep breath, she pulled back one of the gates and slipped through the opening. It clanged shut behind her. She was out of the cage at last and freedom beckoned to her. Bracing her shoulders, her head held high, she stepped out. At first she sang to herself, songs which her father had sung and which had been a part of her life ever since she could remember, but gradually as she grew hotter her throat became drier so she stopped.

There was little or no shade on the road and the sun's rays beat down unmercifully on her uncovered head, her face and the back of her neck. Several times she paused and looked back to the trees which surrounded the houses which clung to the tops of the cliffs and wondered if she should go back, and each time she decided against it.

She had been marching along doggedly for some time when she heard the sound of a car's engine coming from behind her. Someone was coming this way—perhaps a car from one of the other houses. She looked around hopefully and was alarmed when the land about her whirled drunkenly, the mountains seeming to topple sideways. Then everything went black for a second and her head seemed to want to burst. Hand to her head, she blinked rapidly, hoping that everything would become stable again, but the road seemed to have become a see-saw, swinging up and down, and she was falling down towards it, lying on it and swinging up and down, up and down, while her head went round and round.

She must get up before the car came so that she could signal to it to stop. Slowly she managed to roll over and get to her knees, but she couldn't stand up. Every time she tried something seemed to knock her down again. The sound of the car's engine was very loud now, thundering in her ears, and she was in panic in case it ran over her.

Then the engine stopped. A door slammed and she heard a voice speaking to her.

'Señorita, señorita, what is wrong? Why did you leave the house?'

The voice was Carlos's and he was there beside her helping her up, but she couldn't stand properly. She kept wanting to fall down.

'I want to go to Manzanillo. Please take me there?' she said, and her voice sounded peculiar, slurred as if she had had too much to drink.

'No, señorita, you cannot go there. You are ill. I must take you back to the house. Come this way, to the car.'

With his arm about her he urged her forward towards a big white Cadillac. Sebastian Suarez would have a Caddy, she thought, just for Carlos and Manuela to drive to market to fetch home the groceries. Then her head whirled again and nausea heaved in her stomach, and the last thing she knew was Carlos exclaiming in Spanish as he caught her in his arms.

When she came round she was in the house, lying on one of the couches in the blessed coolness of the hall, and Carlos and Manuela were leaning over her. As soon as they saw her eyes were open they spoke to her, one in English and one in Spanish. She asked them again to take her to Manzanillo, told them she didn't want to stay in the gilded cage, but they only shook their heads and then gabbled to each other in Spanish. Dawn tried to sit up and everything whirled about her and she blacked out again.

And so it was for a long time. She kept coming and going while a hammer kept banging away in her head just behind her eyes. Sometimes she was very hot and sometimes she was very cold. Often she was very sick to her stomach. Sometimes she heard a voice talking in a dull monotone and looked around to see who was talking, only to find she was in bed and Manuela was sitting in the chair under the lamp doing her embroidery and it was herself who was muttering feverishly. Once when she came round and felt conscious she saw Sebastian sitting in the chair, the lamplight slanting across his impassive face as he read a book.

But nothing was really clear until she opened her eyes and saw the pale pearly light of dawn streaking the sky beyond the window. Manuela was there, bending over her, and behind her hovered Carlos, his usually inscrutable face creased with anxiety.

'What time is it?' Dawn asked faintly.

'Six-thirty in the morning,' said Carlos.

'What happened?'

'We think a touch of the sun, *señorita*. How you say it? Sunstroke. Also, perhaps, some stomach upset. You have been ill three days. But you are getting better now and will go to sleep.'

It seemed a good idea to go to sleep, so she nodded, closed her eyes and slept at once.

When she awoke she knew it must be past noon because the long window of the room was shuttered against the brilliant sunshine. For a while she lay looking around thinking ruefully that her attempt to leave this house had been a dismal failure. Here she was right back where she had started in this lovely room.

Cautiously she sat up. To her relief her head didn't whirl. She pushed aside the bedclothes and swung her legs out of bed and slid to her feet. She felt a little wobbly, but she made it to the bathroom where above the wash basin she studied her reflection. Pale face, wide grey eyes, slightly slanted, black-lashed, 'put in with a smutty finger', as her father had been fond of telling her, a small straight nose, a soft pink mouth which could be firm, all framed by a cloud of ash-blonde hair.

'What a mess you look!' she whispered to the reflection, and turned on the taps.

After a wash she felt even better and went back to the bedroom to search for the cotton robe and the sandals she had worn the day before. They had gone and there was nothing else for her to wear.

She glanced down at the green nightgown she was wearing. Its lace-edged neckline plunged into a deep V far below her breasts, and the stuff was very sheer so that the outline of her body could be seen through it. She needed a robe to put over it before she ventured out of the bedroom and downstairs to find Manuela and ask her for something more substantial to wear.

There was a long closet covering one wall of the bedroom. Its sliding doors were painted white and gold. Was it possible there were clothes in it? She slid back one of the doors. There were a few women's clothes, including a dressing gown made from thin raw silk. She took it down and slipped it on wondering about those other clothes, about the room and to whom it belonged. To Sebastian Suarez's last mistress, since he didn't have a wife? She almost ripped the dressing gown off at the thought. Then, secretly shocked by the surge of primitive hate for a person who might not even exist, she drew a deep breath to steady herself and tied the sash of the dressing gown tightly round her small waist.

Through the archway she went, stepping out on to the gallery. As she strolled along her glance slanted sideways to the archway which led into the next room, seeing a wide king-sized bed covered in green.

From downstairs came the sound of men's voices speaking in Spanish and the click of leather-soled shoes on tiles. Wandering over to the railings which edged the gallery, Dawn looked down. Near the front door stood Sergeant Moreles. He was just smoothing back his already smooth black hair before putting on his uniform cap and he was talking to Sebastian Suarez.

The sight of the sturdy wide-shouldered figure and crisply curling hair of her rescuer gave Dawn a strange sharp shock. Her heart beat faster and she clung to the railing with one hand. He was back and she was still here, trapped by her own foolishness. If she had had the sense to wait until sundown on Monday before she had tried to walk to Manzanillo she wouldn't have been ill and brought back here by Carlos. She would have been away by now, perhaps even out of the country.

But the policeman was leaving, opening the door and stepping out into the sunshine, and she must stop him.

'Wait, oh, wait for me!' she shouted as loudly as she could, and without waiting to see if either of the men had heard her she hurried along the gallery to the circular staircase. It wasn't possible to go down that quickly, although she tried. As she went round the last curve she lost her balance and fell, rolling down the last few steps to lie in a breathless heap on the tiled floor.

'*Madre di dios!*' Sebastian's voice was sharp and concerned. 'What is it with you that you must always be hurting yourself?'

He helped her to her feet and held her steady, his hands at her waist, his shapely eyebrows tilting with mockery as he looked down at her.

'You're a glutton for punishment, *chiquita*,' he taunted. 'As if it wasn't enough to be half-drowned last Sunday you go walking in the heat on Monday and get sunstroke and now throw yourself downstairs.'

'I didn't throw myself. I tripped, I wanted to speak to the sergeant. I called to him to wait for me. Didn't you hear me?'

'No, I didn't. And now he has gone.' His clear eyes roved over her slowly, searchingly. 'Are you sure you've recovered from the sickness?' he asked gently. 'Do you think you should be up yet?'

'Oh, I'm fine,' she asserted jauntily, and stepped back from him so that his hands were no longer at her waist. He was wearing a casual shirt of pale gold linen and the deep v-neckline revealed the gold chain he wore glinting against his sun-dark, hair-sprinkled chest. Trousers of thick cream-coloured cotton were moulded close to his

lean hips and heavy thighs. He was strong, handsome
and excitingly attractive to her, so she stepped back
further, afraid of that attraction.

'I wish I could have spoken to Sergeant Moreles,' she
said. 'He could have taken me to Manzanillo.'

'Dressed like that?' he scoffed, amusement glinting in
his eyes. 'Why do you want to go there all the time?
Carlos says that when he found you on the road you
kept going on about it.' He moved towards her and
raised a hand to lift a tress of her hair which swung beside her cheek and tuck it behind her ear. 'Didn't I warn
you you'd be hurt if you tried to fly away, pretty bird?'
he murmured gently. 'Why didn't you take notice of
what I said to you?'

Her glance faltered before the intentness of his and she
moved away from him, away from the fingers which had
lingered against her cheek and her ear when he had
pushed back her hair. She went to the edge of the pool
and looked down into its silvery green depths, seeing tiny
striped tropical fish flicking slowly and elegantly in and
out of trailing water plants.

'You should have told me Sergeant Moreles was here,'
she said, ignoring his question because she had no answer
to it, at least not one she wanted him to hear. 'He brought
news of the rented car, didn't he?'

'*Si*, but when I told him you had been ill he asked me
not to disturb you,' he replied easily.

'But I should have had the news first-hand from him,
not through you,' she retorted, swinging round to look
at him.

'Whether it comes to you directly from him or through
me it isn't good news,' he said quietly, and reaching out
a hand, grasped one of hers. 'Come and sit down and I
will tell you.'

For a moment she was tempted to resist the pull he exerted on her hand. She didn't want to sit with him on one of the luxurious velvet couches. She didn't want to be close to him because she didn't trust the reaction of her own senses to his warm vibrancy. But anxiety about the car and about Farley overrode that fear and she went with him to curl up in a corner of the divan, her feet tucked beneath her. Removing her hand from his, she pushed it into the wide kimono sleeve of the dressing gown.

He sat close to her, one leg bent so that it rested on the padded seat the knee just touching her bent-up bare legs, one arm stretched out so that his hand rested on the back of the couch. In that position he faced her and she was more or less trapped in the corner of the divan. He seemed in no hurry to tell her what the policeman had told him and for a while they studied each other in silence, with a sort of intimate curiosity, as if they had expected changes to have taken place in the past few days.

Dawn broke the silence, made nervous by the tension between them.

'What did Sergeant Moreles say?' she muttered, pulling the skirt of the dressing gown over her legs.

'That the car has been found abandoned in Acapulco. There was no sign of your friend or his companion.'

'And my purse and clothes? Were they in it?'

'There was nothing in it and the petrol tank was empty. The police are assuming that when they ran out of gas Farley and Brett just left it by the side of the road making sure to take anything which would incriminate them. The Sergeant is arranging to have the car returned to the rental agency in Los Angeles.'

'Oh, but. . . .' She broke off, flashed him a wary glance and chewed on her lower lip.

'Oh, but what?' he prompted.

'Won't there be some payment to be made on the hiring of the car and the expense of returning it?'

'*Si*. I will pay it for you.'

'Thank you. I'm very grateful! And one day I'll pay you back.'

'*No importa*.' He shrugged his shoulders. 'It won't be necessary for you to do that.'

'But I must. I always like to pay my debts.' She broke off as she realised how much she had been hoping that the car would have contained her money, her passport. Now there was no doubt she had nothing, and she should never have trusted Farley in the first place.

'Oh, what am I going to do?' she whispered. 'What am I going to do?'

'I've told you, *chiquita*, you can stay with me,' was the imperturbable reply.

'And I've told you that I can't,' she retorted.

'Not even to pay that large debt you owe me, hmm?' he challenged, and her eyes fell before his bright ironic glance.

'I have to find Judy,' she muttered. 'I promised Dad I would find her.'

'How will you do that if you have no money and no means of earning any?' he demanded.

'I don't know yet, but I'll find a way,' she replied with a lift of her chin.

'You'll also find a way if you stay with me,' he said smoothly. 'Have you forgotten? Robert Suarez is my half-brother. I can take you to meet someone who will know where he is.'

She stared at him, wanting to trust him, yet strangely suspicious of him.

'Will you please take me to meet this someone?' she asked at last, hesitantly.

'Maybe tomorrow, maybe the next day,' he replied

with a shrug. 'But I'll only do it if you'll do something for me, by way of paying off the debt you owe me, you know the big one which puts you in such a great obligation to me and which you'd like so much to clear?' The dryness in his voice mocked her.

'You mean you'd want me to be your ... your companion?' she whispered, not looking at him, plucking nervously at the silk which covered her knees. He covered her nervous fiddling fingers with his hand, as he had done once before, and held them in his warm comforting grasp.

'I want you to be more than that,' he said softly, and she glanced up to find he was leaning close to her, so close she could smell the subtle tangy fragrance of his skin and when he spoke again his lips almost touched hers, but not quite. 'I want you to be my wife,' he whispered.

Shock jarred through her and she jerked back from the temptation of those bold lips which given half a chance would possess hers. If she could have jumped up from the couch she would have done, but she was trapped in the corner. Her eyes were wide with disbelief as she searched the lean dark face poised above hers for any sign of mockery. There was none. His eyes were clear and coldly calculating and once again she thought of an eagle watching its prey, calmly waiting for it to run in panic before swooping down on it. If she tried to run now he would swoop, and once she felt his arms around her... ?

Shaken suddenly by a sick surge of excitement at the memory of the way his hard arms had held her and the way his lips had lit a flame in her, she looked down again.

'You don't know what you're saying,' she accused, hoping to divert him by implying that he was unstable, and from under her lashes she watched the slow mocking smile she was beginning to like curve his mouth.

'But I do, *chiquita*. I know very well. I would like to marry and I am asking you if you would like to marry me. I realise it is rather sudden, this proposal of mine, but circumstances have dictated that I move more quickly than I had intended. Now tell me, what do you think of the idea?'

'I think it's crazy,' she spluttered.

'So you have doubts about my sanity, do you?' he said with a self-mocking grin. 'Why is it crazy?'

'We hardly know each other.'

'For that I'm glad,' he retorted. 'To marry someone one has known for a long time must be infinitely boring.'

'And we come from different cultures. We have different attitudes to many things,' she continued. 'We would quarrel.'

'You think so? Why?'

'Well, for instance, you believe in *machismo*, in the superiority of the male, and I believe women to be equal to men.' She felt his thumb caress the inside of her wrist and the delicious tingle raced along her nerves. She glanced up to object and met the glinting mocking gaze of his black-lashed eyes. He knew what effect that subtle caress had on her. 'Please don't do that,' she said sharply, and tried to free her hand. When his fingers tightened she gave him a glare designed to shrivel him. 'You see, you regard me as a plaything,' she accused.

'No, not a play*thing*, but a play*mate*, with emphasis on the word mate,' he replied smoothly, with a wicked grin. 'I told you how I feel about you last Monday, that I would like you to stay and be my companion, but you didn't care for my arrangement. My feelings haven't changed. I still want you, so I'm offering a more legal arrangement. As for the *machismo*,' he shrugged his broad shoulders, 'it isn't important to me. I believe only that I'm superior to you in physical strength and right now in my ability to protect you, and I'm offering to use that strength and that ability on your behalf if you will marry me.'

'But ... we're not in love,' she protested.

His thumb stopped caressing her wrist and he gave her a narrow-eyed sceptical glance.

'What do you know about love?' he jeered. 'Very little, I suspect. Do you imagine yourself to be in love with this Farley you talk about? Is he the one who turns you on, lights up your life?'

'No, he doesn't,' she admitted, and gave him another apprehensive glance, thinking of the effect he had on her, the way the nerves of her stomach fluttered at the sight of him. With one kiss he had turned her on, made her come alive in a way she had never felt before. But surely that didn't mean she was in love with him. Surely that was only physical desire which he had admitted, honestly enough, was what he felt for her.

'Is there someone else, then? Someone in Canada?' he asked.

'No.'

'So you are not in love with anyone. *Bueno*.' He sounded complacent. 'That is how I hoped it would be.' He looked down at their entwined hands and said quietly, 'I told Sergeant Moreles that you and I are going to be married.'

'Oh, you had no right to do that. I ... I ... haven't accepted your proposal,' she protested.

'But you're going to, aren't you, *querida*?' he said, and his glance drifted over her slowly, sensuously enquiring, so that sweet shivers tingled through her as if he had touched her.

'Am I?' she countered shakily. 'What makes you think I am?' Smiling a little, he leaned towards her again until his hard chest was pressing against the sensitive tips of her breasts.

'Because you're not going to be able to help yourself,' he murmured, and then his lips closed over hers.

For a moment she struggled against the surge of wild excitement which beat through her, but his lips grew harder and she felt his teeth crushing her lips. Then came that leaping flame along her nerves and she was lost. Her hands, untutored in the ways of loving, found the opening of his shirt and her fingers strayed shyly against the warm pulsing skin of his throat as she strained against him, giving her mouth to his. More expert than hers, his fingers slid under the edge of the thin silk dressing gown she wore and fanned out tenderly over her breast so that she gasped.

When he withdrew she leaned back against the end of the couch and covered her face with her hands.

'So when shall we be married, hmm?' His voice, slightly breathless, held a soft taunt. 'Tomorrow? Or the next day? The sooner the better, I should think, for that cold northern morality of yours.'

The taunt flicked her on the raw and she moaned a little, then felt his hands on her wrists pulling her hands away from her face.

'Ah, come, *chiquita*,' he said comfortingly. 'There is nothing to be ashamed of. I don't think any the less of you because you respond to my kisses. Now what do you say? Do you agree? Will you marry me, tomorrow, and then we'll find out where Roberto is so you can ask him about your sister?'

Dawn looked down at the hands holding hers. Why did he want to marry her? There must be another reason than the one he had given her. She looked up into his eyes. They were watching her and he was smiling again as if he knew all about the struggle which was going on within her.

'You see how you bring out the best in me?' he said, his mouth taking on a more ironic curve. 'Never before have I asked a woman to marry me. I have never had any need to.'

She could believe that. He had probably taken what he wanted from a woman when and where he had wanted it, like the bold Spanish Conquistadors had done when they had first come to this country. And since he could employ servants to look after his household affairs he had no need of a housewife. Why then did he want to marry her?

'What will you do if I say no?' she asked.

'Nothing.' He spoke curtly and his face hardened, stiffening with pride.

'You mean...?'

'I mean what I say. I'll do nothing. I won't help you to find your sister and I won't help you to leave here. But I'll expect you to be gone by tomorrow morning,' he replied in a cool voice. 'Perhaps this will help you to make up your mind. Marry me and you'll have a new identity, a Mexican one, and you'll have a much better chance of finding your sister. Refuse to marry me and you can leave here tomorrow morning, but if you run into trouble with the authorities because you're in this country without a passport, without money and without a tourist card don't appeal to me for help. I'll do nothing.'

'An ultimatum?' she challenged, her chin up.

'Si, an ultimatum,' he replied, his mouth curving with

humour again. 'So what is your answer?'

Dawn looked around the cool silvery green hall, her eyes flickering a little wildly as if she were searching for a way of escape. She felt suddenly very weak and helpless.

'I don't know. I can't think. I must have more time to think,' she muttered, her hand to her head. 'I haven't had anything to eat for days.'

'Then you shall eat now,' he replied practically, letting go of her hands and rising to his feet. 'Manuela will prepare something for you. And you can have more time to think. I'm going surfing now. I'll see you later and at dinner you can give me your answer.'

CHAPTER THREE

STILL sitting on the grey velvet couch beside the shimmering dimpling pool, Dawn ate a *taco* stuffed with delicious shrimps and covered by a tangy sauce, chose a banana from a dish of fresh fruit and drank cupfuls of smooth *café con leche*, coffee made with freshly boiled milk. Carlos brought the food, setting it out on a round glass-topped table which he had placed close beside her. He left her alone and went through an archway screened by two small palm trees which grew in large earthenware tubs set on the tiled floor, but hardly had she finished eating than he appeared again swinging his tray and she could not help wondering if he had been watching her from behind the palm trees so that he would know exactly when to come and clear away the empty dishes.

'You have finished, *señorita*?' he asked politely.

'Yes, thank you.' She watched his small neat hands moving deftly then looked at his dark olive-skinned face and wondered what he was thinking. Here was another person to whom she owed a debt of gratitude. If he hadn't missed her on Monday afternoon and hadn't followed her she might have been very ill indeed, could even have died out there on the wide road from exposure and thirst.

'I am very grateful,' she began in a sudden burst of speech, and broke off as he raised his head and looked at her, his dark eyes unrevealing as ever.

'*Perdonme, no entiende.* Pardon me, *señorita,* I don't understand this word "grateful," ' he said, with a frown.

'I ... I want to say thank you to you ... and to Manuela for ... for what you have done for me,' she said slowly. '*Muchas gracias.*'

A little gleam appeared in the black eyes, but no smile touched his mouth.

'*De nada, señorita,*' he said. 'Don't mention it, Manuela and I do what Señor Suarez tell us to do. He say we must look after you, see that you are comfortable at all times.' A thin vertical line creased his forehead as he frowned. 'You will not try to walk to Manzanillo again, *señorita.* It is a long way.'

'How far?' she asked.

'About fifty kilometres.'

'And Guadalajara?'

'Perhaps two hundred.' He shrugged his shoulders. 'I am not sure.'

'How do you get there?'

'Me?' He looked vaguely surprised.

'*Si,* if you or Manuela want to go to Manzanillo or any other town, how do you go.'

'We go in the car, *señorita,* the one I was driving yesterday.'

'You don't use the bus, then?'

'There is no bus from here. To get the bus you have to go to Manzanillo.'

'When will you and Manuela go shopping next?' she asked.

'Maybe tomorrow, maybe the next day. *Quien sabe?*' He lifted his hands in a gesture of fatalism. 'Who knows when we shall go? When Manuela says.'

'If you go tomorrow to Manzanillo will you take me with you?'

The broad dark face became once again as inscrutable as any stone statue's. The dark eyes were blank. He picked up his laden tray and swung it to his shoulder.

'No, *señorita*, if we go we will not take you,' he said coolly. 'We do only what Señor Suarez tells us to do. Excuse me, *por favor.*'

He went off and Dawn sat staring at the pool with her hands clenching slowly on her knees as frustration boiled within her. So Carlos and Manuela did only what Señor Suarez told them to do, did they? And presumably he had told them to watch her and see that she didn't leave the house. Carlos hadn't come after her on Monday afternoon and brought her back here because he had been concerned about her walking in the heat. He had followed her and brought her back because if she hadn't been in the house when his employer returned from Guadalajara he would have been reprimanded, might even have been dismissed from his job; a job which no doubt was well paid, easy and comfortatble for both him and his wife.

Oh, what was she going to do? How was she going to get away from here? If she refused to marry Sebastian she would have to go tomorrow morning anyway, but how? Elbows on her knees and chin in her hand, she considered his suggestion she should marry him. She still thought it was crazy. Marriages between people who had only just met, who were as different from one another as she and he were, didn't happen, except in romances, when something magical happened and they fell in love, something wonderful and transforming which lit up their lives.

Her fingers uncurled and spread over her face and she closed her eyes with a little groan as the nerves in the pit of her stomach contracted suddenly, sending that sick surge of excitement through her, a tingling which spread upwards to the very tips of her breasts. It seemed she had only to think of him now and it happened. She didn't have to see him or be with him to want him. He had touched her and something wonderful and transforming had happened to her. Her hand moved down to slide under the robe and touch her breast. No one had touched her like he had. No man had made her feel this way. But then she hadn't known a man like him before, strong, autocratic, blatantly sensual yet essentially generous and compassionate, possessing an endearing quality of being able to make fun of himself, a man she could live with and love.

Love? What did she know about love, the sort of love which could happen, so she had read and had been told, between a man and a woman? Was this feeling of sick rapture which surged through her part of that sort of love? Or was it just animal desire roused in her by an expert in lovemaking, by a man who had been conceived by a passionate, reckless love?

If only she had some experience or someone of her own to talk to about how she felt. If only she could talk to Judy. *Judy!* Her dizzy mind groped for and held on to the name. It was because of Judy she was here, washed up on the edge of Sebastian Suarez's life. She must find

Judy and he had said he would help her to find her sister if she promised to marry him. So why not marry him? Why hesitate?

'*Señorita?*' Manuela's soft slow voice spoke to her and she looked up to find the woman standing there patiently, holding the cotton gown across her held-out arms.

'Oh. *Si, muchas gracias.*' Dawn got to her feet and took the gown. It had been washed and ironed and the embroidered flowers were shiny and bright. 'I will go and put it on,' she said, futilely because Manuela wouldn't understand a word of what she had said, and the woman nodded and smiled and went away past the palm trees.

Upstairs in the pretty bathroom Dawn washed, cleaned her teeth with the toothbrush and toothpaste thoughtfully provided, dressed in the cotton gown again and brushed her hair. Satisfied that she looked as clean and neat as possible, she went down the circular staircase to the hall again. Carlos was there pruning and watering one of the azalea plants, presumably hovering about to see that she didn't leave the house without his knowledge.

'I'm going to the beach,' she said to him, 'to watch Señor Suarez surfing. I shall use the steps going down from the terrace.'

'*Si, señorita.*'

He nearly smiled, she thought, as she went through the *salón* and stepped out on to the terrace, into the hot humid air, fragrant with the scent of many flowers.

'You wear this, *señorita, por favor.*' Carlos was beside her, although she hadn't heard him follow her, and he was handing her a straw hat with a high conical crown and a broad curled over brim.

'Thank you,' she said, and tried smiling at him as she placed it on her head. Somehow she had to break through that tough, morose façade of his. His lips did twitch a little, she thought, and a gleam came and went in his eyes, but all he said was the usual offhand, 'De nada.'

Down the winding steps she went, brushing by the stiff rustling leaves of the palms until she stepped on to the soft golden sand. There she stopped and looked along the beach, half expecting to see the noisy group of scantily-dressed young Americans which had been on it last Sunday afternoon. But there were only a few people, mostly children with parents or baby-sitters sitting under the palms, between which fishing nets were hung to dry, or splashing and shouting in the sea.

Slowly, her feet sinking in the silky glittering sand, Dawn wandered along, turning her head once to look over her shoulder towards the steps. Yes, Carlos was standing there watching her, not trusting her. Her lips tightened. She had a good mind to give him a run for his money, pretend she was leaving again. She glanced round to where the few cars which had brought the families down to the beach were parked. She would make for those, hide behind one of them and watch what he did. She glanced back to see if he was still there watching her. Yes, he was. She turned, began to run and collided head on with a person who was racing down the beach towards the water. Big hands caught her shoulders and steadied her and a young, slightly breathless masculine voice said in English,

'Whew ... I'm sorry! Guess I wasn't looking where I was going—I was so keen to get into that surf. You okay, lady?'

For a moment she thought he was Farley with his soft Californian drawl and his untidy floss of light blond hair. But he was shorter than Farley, more stockily built, and he was younger, about seventeen, not twenty-seven.

'I'm afraid I wasn't looking where I was going either,' she said with a smile, and his grey eyes narrowed with interest.

'I haven't seen you around here before,' he remarked, and his glance lifted beyond her briefly, then came back to study her again. 'You staying at the Suarez place?'

'Yes, I am.'

'Friend of Sebastian Suarez?'

'I ... er ... in a way,' she stammered, saw him grin knowingly, and added in a rush, 'but not in the way you're thinking.' A sudden idea flashed into her mind. 'Did you come here by car?'

'No. Mother and I flew down this morning from L. A. That's our place ... the one like a birthday cake, all pink icing.' He pointed to a villa half hidden by trees which was set back from the narrow beach road. 'Why do you ask?'

'I'm looking for a way to get to Manzanillo,' she said.

'Then why don't you ask old Carlos there to drive you in?' he replied.

Dawn glanced over her shoulder. Carlos was still standing at the bottom of the steps, his white coat glimmering in the shade of the trees which drooped from the cliffside over the beach. Then she turned back to the young man and for the first time in her life tried using her feminine wiles. Sighing and letting her eyelashes flutter down, she made her mouth curve petulantly.

'I have, and he won't,' she murmured, and watched for the effect on him through her lashes. His blond eyebrows shot up in surprise and his glance went sideways towards the ocean.

'How about Sebastian?' he asked.

'He won't, either.' She licked her lips with the tip of her tongue and looked up at him pleadingly. 'Oh, please, will you help me? I must get away from here. I'll tell you all about it on the way.'

'Now?' he exclaimed. 'You want to go now?'

'No,' she began. 'Tomorrow would. . . .'

'Look, lady,' he interrupted her suddenly, 'you're very nice and pretty, but I came here to ride the surf, not to drive strange girls about.' And turning abruptly, he went leaping down to the thundering crashing surf.

Dawn watched him go, her shoulders slumping in defeat as she realised why he had run away. Sebastian was walking up from the sea carrying his surfboard over one shoulder. Drops of water spangled his wet clustering curls and a golden chain and medallion glinted against his sun-bronzed hair-sprinkled chest. Brief black bikini swimming shorts only just saved him from being completely nude. She dragged her greedy glance away from the attractions of his lean muscular body and looked up at golden eyes hard and bright glinting at her from between thick black lashes and at firm chiselled lips which were curving back over square white teeth in a smile of lazy mockery.

'Toby's a friendly young guy but not very obliging,' he said tauntingly, and slid a cool damp hand down her arm to grasp her hand with his. 'You were trying to fly away again?'

'Yes,' she replied, her head held high. 'Are you surprised?'

'No, not really, because I realise that yours is a spirit which doesn't like to be constrained,' he replied, his face suddenly very serious. 'But I'm a little hurt.'

'Hurt?' she exclaimed, wishing that they were standing anywhere but on that public beach with the thunderous sound of the surf making quiet talk impossible and with curious eyes of women and children watching them. 'Why?'

'Because I was hoping that by now you would be getting used to the idea of staying with me,' he replied, and bending his head quickly, kissed her on the mouth, taking her lips in a flagrant act of possession which set rebellion flaring through her even while she felt that swift flame racing along the fuse of her nerves to set off an explosion of desire which weakened her so that she had to lean against him for support, her hands catching at the muscle-ridged hardness of his arms. And her fingers, liking the feel of his sea-cool skin, moved sensuously, almost hungrily, wanting to feel more of him.

'Why did you do that?' she whispered when his mouth lifted from hers yet still remained close.

'To show Toby and anyone else on this beach who might be interested just how things are between you and me,' he replied, and before she could do anything about it he kissed her again, a swift taunting kiss which left her breathless and clinging. 'Want to do something about it?' he scoffed, when it was done and she was glaring at him helplessly. 'Want to tell me to go to hell or slap my face?'

'And give you some reason to show off your superior strength?' she retorted, breaking free of him and wiping her hand across her mouth. 'Not likely!' she seethed, and he laughed at her. A movement caught her eyes and she glanced sideways. The young man Toby was standing quite near on the edge of the surf, his back to the sea, his hands on his hips, and was staring at her and Sebastian. Her glance wandered further round. Several tawny-skinned, black-haired, black-eyed children were also staring at her and giggling. She turned on Sebastian. 'Oh, I think I hate you!' she cried, and swinging round she floundered over the soft sand towards the cliff, knowing that Toby would never believe that she wanted to get away now.

Carlos wasn't at the bottom of the steps, but he was on the terrace when she reached it. He was pretending to cut off the dead roses from the bushes which clustered along the wall. He turned to glance at her as she hurried towards the *salón* window. Half-way across the room she turned to look and he was there following her. He didn't follow her up the spiral staircase, nor did he watch her go along the gallery to the bedroom but pretended to be attending to the azaleas again.

In the shuttered quietness of the bedroom Dawn flung herself across the bed and buried her head on her folded arms, listening to the frantic beating of her heart. Perspiration was beading her forehead and her hair was limp with it. Groaning, she rolled over and sat up. It must be the tropical climate which was making her behave so irrationally, causing her emotions to explode like firecrackers and awakening in her an awareness of her own sexuality. She had never behaved like this before, shouting at a man that she hated him while all the time her senses were clamouring to be with him, to give herself in sweet reckless abandonment.

She knew why she had told him she hated him. She recognised the power he had to defeat her. But she must try to cool down and think sensibly. In a few hours she would have to answer his ultimatum. Agree to marry him or be turned out to find her own way to Manzanillo or some other centre, there to begin the uphill task of explaining to the Mexican authorities that although she was in this country quite legally she had been robbed of all her possessions.

She lay on the bed a long time thinking, only becoming aware that night had come when light slanted into the room through the archway from the gallery. Hands under head, she lay in the sort of hazy contentment which coming to a decision had brought to her. She would marry Sebastian Suarez. She would be his wife as he had requested and in return he would help her find her sister.

Rolling off the bed, she went into the bathroom and turned on the bath taps. In a few minutes she was relaxing in foam up to her chin. She washed her hair and feeling refreshed stood up in the bath to examine her reflection in the mirrors around it, looking critically for flaws in her appearance. Never had she looked at herself in such a way before, but then she was doing many things for the first time in her life since she had come to this house.

Maybe it was the sunshine which had liberated her, had thawed out her inhibitions? Almost at once she ridiculed the idea of being liberated. Since she had been saved from the ocean by Sebastian and brought here to this gilded cage of a house she had lost her freedom. She had lost her youthful immunity to the powerful forces of sexual attraction and she was now trapped here by her own desires.

In the bedroom she found the hair-dryer and blew her hair dry. Then she dressed in the cotton gown again and was putting the touches to the arrangement of her hair when Sebastian's reflection appeared in the mirror. Laying down the comb, she watched him come up behind her, apprehension leaping along her nerves.

He was wearing dark light-weight slacks and a magnificent shirt made from soft white silk. Its fullness was gathered into a deep shoulder saddle and the wide sleeves were caught at the wrist by neat cuffs. Both saddle and cuffs were embroidered with Mexican designs, as was the wide collar. Its opening was a deep slit down the front going almost to the waist where a hand-tooled leather belt cinched the shirt to his leanness.

'You're not going to wear that cotton rag to eat dinner with me,' he said autocratically, taking her by the shoulder and spinning her round to face him, and as usual rebellion at such high-handed treatment flared with her.

'I like it,' she retorted. 'It's very pretty and Manuela embroidered it herself.'

'So what if Manuela did embroider it herself? It's like a sack and does nothing for you.' He turned away and slid open the closet, reached in and took down a gown of shimmering dark green silk. He laid it on the bed. 'Wear that,' he ordered crisply.

'No!' Her refusal rang out clearly as she stared with revulsion at the lovely dress.

'Why not?' Hands on his hips, he stared at her across the width of the bed.

'I'm not going to wear a gown which has been worn by another woman,' she retorted.

'What other woman?' he queried, frowning at her.

'Your ... your last mistress!' she quavered, and his eyebrows went up in haughty disdain.

'*Dios*, you're inconsistent,' he drawled. 'That cotton rag you're wearing belongs to Manuela's daughter, another woman, yet you don't object to it. This gown is new,' he pointed at the green one on the bed. 'I bought it for you in Guadalajara and I'm interested to see if it fits.'

'You bought it for me?' she said incredulously, and rebellion flared up again. 'Oh, you had no right to buy me clothes. No right at all.'

'But, *chiquita*,' he sounded tolerantly amused as he came round the bed to stand in front of her, 'you have no clothes of your own. I bought this for you and the dressing gown you were wearing earlier, and the other dress and the linen suit which are hanging in the closet. Manuela hung them in there. Didn't she tell you?'

'I must have been asleep when she brought them in,' she muttered. 'But you still had no right to buy them for me. You're far too arrogant and domineering, far too fond of having your own way.'

He shrugged his shoulders and spread his hands in a fatalistic gesture.

'I am as I am,' he replied. 'So now you know this gown is for you, you will wear it, hmm? And I'll see you by the pool in a few minutes.'

He had gone from the room before Dawn had time to think up a retort. Anyway, might as well save her breath. He didn't care a hang what she thought of him. She could tell him he was arrogant and had no rights over her until she was blue in the face, but he was only going to either laugh at her or ignore her and go his own way. His self-confidence was overpowering and it grated on her.

She looked at the green dress. She was very tempted to defy him further, refuse to put it on and stay in her room, refuse to join him for dinner. Yes, very tempted, even at the risk of missing a meal and going to bed hungry, just to see what he would do.

The whisper of rope-soled sandals heralded the arrival of Manuela, who entered the room without ceremony, making Dawn wish the house wasn't so open, that there were a few doors to close and give privacy. Manuela pointed to the green gown and looked across at her.

'*Buenas noches, señorita*,' she said, and lifted the gown by its shoulders. 'I 'elp you,' she added very slowly, and then smiled a wide dazzling smile which changed her whole face.

'No, thank you. *No, muchas gracias*,' said Dawn coldly. Manuela's smile faded and she looked very sad.

'*Si, señorita*, I 'elp you. Señor Suarez....' She broke off and then burst into a spate of Spanish, waving her hands about while tears spurted from her big dark eyes and ran down her face, much to Dawn's amazement.

'Okay, okay,' said Dawn, rushing forward and speaking the one word she knew the woman would understand at once. 'Okay, you can help me,' she said. 'Only please don't cry, please don't cry.' And to show she meant what she said she began to pull the cotton gown over her head.

Almost at once Manuela's tears stopped and her wide smile appeared again, like the sun shining through the rain, and when the cotton gown was off she slipped the silky green evening dress over Dawn's head.

It was expensively simple, with a sleeveless halter bodice which left her back bare and plunged in a deep V right down to her waist in front so that her small breasts were only just covered. The rich dark colour played up the whiteness of her skin and set off the silvery torch of of her hair and in the long mirror she looked so different from usual that she could only stare in surprise.

Manuela stood back eyeing her critically and gabbled in Spanish, twitched the full skirt of the gown this way and that, stood back again and smiled.

'*Me gusta, muy bonita*,' she said. '*Veni, señorita*.' She gestured towards the archway.

'In a little while,' said Dawn, and Manuela frowned in a puzzled way. '*Dentre di poco*,' said Dawn slowly, and the woman nodded.

'*Si, señorita*,' she said, and left the room.

She couldn't go down to join Sebastian in the hall by the pool yet, thought Dawn, because she had to get used to this new self. Strange how a few pieces of coloured material could change one's appearance. She had never taken much interest in clothes, had always worn shirts and jeans when in her teens and slack suits when she had gone out to work as a typist for a publishing company. Judy had been the one who had dressed up, had believed in emphasising her femininity in order to draw the attention of the opposite sex, and it had often been a source of disagreement between them when Dawn had criticised her for playing up to male chauvinism.

How could she go down and face Sebastian wearing this flattering gown which hinted so much at what it concealed? She imagined how his eyes would glint and his mouth would take on that wanton curve as his gaze roved over her possessively. No, she couldn't go. She was too shy. If only she had a little of her sister's confidence, could put on an act and pretend she was used to dressing like this and dining tête-à-tête with a man who had admitted quite honestly that he found her physically attractive.

She wouldn't go down and if anyone came looking for her she would pretend she felt ill again, that her head was still aching. Her mouth quirked into a rueful grin. Now she was behaving in a typically feminine fashion! A headache had always been a woman's way of avoiding a confrontation or a proposal of marriage.

Up and down the room she paced, the skirt of the gown rustling about her bare legs as she struggled with herself, and almost half an hour had gone by before she came reluctantly to the decision to go down and give Sebastian her answer, telling herself all the time it was for Judy's sake.

She left the room quickly before she could change her mind again, sped along the gallery, then paused, hand on the railing, to look down. He was just below her, standing beside the pool looking down into it. Light winked on the facets of the cut glass tumbler he was holding when he raised it to his lips and drained it. He moved, went over to one of the round glass-topped tables, lifted a decanter and poured liquor into the glass, drank from it, looked up and saw her.

Slowly he paced across until he was standing below her again and raised his glass to her.

'I drink to you, *señorita*. You look charming,' he drawled. He drank half the liquor in the glass then his eyes glinted up at her again. 'Are you coming down? Or are you hoping I'll come and fetch you?'

His mood was unpredictable, Dawn could see. Because she had kept him waiting? Or because of the liquor he had drunk? Her glance went uneasily to the decanter on the table and back to the glass in his hand, then to his face. His grin mocked her.

'It's *tequila*,' he said. 'And you're quite right, I have drunk too much of it. You see, I don't like being kept waiting. So if I behave badly you have only yourself to blame. You should have come down sooner.' He turned away. 'But what would you like to drink? Nothing alcoholic, I'm sure. Lemonade, tamarind or Jamaica flower juice? Or perhaps the inevitable Coke?' he asked dryly.

She had a feeling he had turned against her for some reason, had decided he didn't like her after all. Perhaps she had gone too far that afternoon by telling him she hated him and later by accusing him of arrogance. Perhaps he had taken offence and now didn't want to help her any more. It would just be her luck, she thought, for him to have changed his mind and have decided he didn't want to marry her when she had decided to accept his proposal.

She became aware that he was still waiting for her to answer his enquiry, an expression of impatience thinning his mouth. And that Carlos had appeared with his usual magic and was waiting too.

'Lemonade, please,' she gasped, and hurried along to the spiral staircase. By the time she reached the hall Carlos was returning from the kitchen carrying a tall frosted glass on a silver tray. He came right up to her. She took the glass which clinked with ice and seemed to freeze her fingers, and thanked him. He inclined his head and went away, disappearing beyond the potted palms.

'A cool innocent drink for a cool innocent virgin,' murmured Sebastian provocatively, coming to stand close to her, and she flashed him an upward wary glance. The lighting in the hallway was subtly arranged to make the place seem seductively intimate, but she could very clearly see the glitter of mockery in his eyes. She raised her glass and sipped some of the cold bittersweet drink, hoping that if she refused to rise to the bait he had trailed before her he would refrain from making any more provocative remarks. But as she lowered the glass he slid his fingers around the bottom of it and took it from her. Still watching her with narrowed eyes, he drank from it.

'Cool, innocent, seemingly sweet, with an acid kick to it—just like you, *chiquita*,' he taunted, handing the glass back to her and raising his own to his lips and drinking from it. 'I think I prefer my own native potion even if it is likely to give me a sore head in the morning. It fires the blood, not chills it.'

'If that's your opinion of me,' she retorted, moving away from him and going to stand at the edge of the pool, 'I wonder that you've asked me to marry you.'

'I admit I am wondering too,' he murmured, and she felt dismay stab her like a knife. Turning slowly, she looked at him, hoping to see that he was smiling that half-sweet, half-malicious smile which would mean he was teasing her. But he was standing too far away from her to see his face clearly. Above the white shimmer of his shirt it was a dark mask.

'H-have you changed your mind?' she asked hesitantly.

'Is that strange quiver in your voice expressive of hope or disappointment?' he parried mockingly. He went over to the table again and the decanter clinked against his tumbler as he poured more liquor into it. He sipped from the glass, looking across at her with narrowed eyes. 'Is it possible you have come to a decision at last?' he taunted.

'Yes, I have, but if you've changed your mind there's no point in my telling you about it, is there?' she retorted, doing her best to keep her voice cool and light although her emotions were swirling about like a whirlpool, hate and desire, hope and disappointment all curdling within her making her feel very bewildered. Never had anyone been able to torment her as this man was doing!

'Yet, I think I would like to hear what it is,' he murmured, and setting his half-empty glass down on the table came towards her slowly. A few feet away from her he stopped, tipped his head to one side and considered her, his glance going over her in a cool assessing way which brought the red flags of rebellion flaring into her cheeks. How she hated being looked over!

'The gown becomes you as I guessed it might,' he drawled, and moved towards her again.

'I wish you wouldn't look at me like that,' she seethed.

'Like what?' The note of surprise in his voice sounded genuine.

'As if ... as if....' She broke off to swallow, then blurted, 'I'm not a possession of yours!'

'You believe I look at you as if you are?' he queried, his eyebrows lifting in surprise. 'But you're mistaken.

I was looking at the dress only, admiring my own good taste. . . .'

'Oh, you. . .!' she gasped, driven beyond endurance by his taunting, and raising her glass she threw its contents in the direction of his dark derisive face. Lemonade and ice cubes spattered him. She saw his eyes blaze at her, realised what she had done and tossing the glass aside, not caring where it fell, she ran across the hall to the front door, wrenched it open and stepped out into the balmy night air.

The door closed behind her and she ran down the steps. Along the driveway towards the road she hurried instinctively, stopped to catch her breath and looked back. No one was following her. Above her in the black velvet tropical sky the stars glittered like huge yellow diamonds and all about her in the darkness of the garden cicadas were singing their night song. But someone else was singing too. A pleasant tenor voice was raised in a haunting romantic song and it was accompanied by the passionate throbbing of guitars.

For a few moments Dawn stood still, held spellbound by the song of love. The singer's voice seemed to be coming from the opposite direction and in the warm starlit night his message was clear even though he was singing in a language of which she had only the slightest knowledge. He was enticing his lady to come out and make love with him.

Curiosity to see who was singing overcame her initial instinct to run away while the going was good. She followed the driveway past the front of the house and round to the wing where she guessed Manuela and Carlos lived above the kitchen and the storage rooms. At the corner of the house where trees cast a shadow she paused and peeped round. In the light shafting from a window on to the lawn she could see three men standing. All of them were wearing wide-brimmed, conical-crowned Mexican hats, short jackets over white shirts and trousers which had decorative glittering stripes down the outside seams, and all of them were playing guitars.

While Dawn watched in amazement the song came to an end. The three men consulted with each other, came to some decision and began to play their guitars again, strumming an introduction to yet another song. The singer's voice, sad and sweet, soared up in a heart-stealing serenade.

As she stood there listening Dawn felt unbearable longings stir within her. If only the sort of love which the music expressed really existed! If only that was how Sebastian Suarez felt about her it would be so easy for her to tell him she would marry him. But he didn't. He wouldn't torment her if he loved her. And anyway, she could hardly expect him to have fallen in love with her in such a short time. After all, she hadn't fallen in love with him and she had only decided to accept his proposal because marriage to him would apparently provide her with the means to an end: the means for finding Judy.

The second song ended on a note of passionate entreaty. Sighing to herself, Dawn turned away and found Carlos standing behind her.

'The dinner is ready to be served, *señorita*,' he said in his inscrutable way. 'You come now?'

'*Si*. I like this singing,' she said, falling into step beside him, wondering vaguely why all her desire to run away had gone. 'Who are those men?'

'They are troubadors, *señorita*. This State of Jalisco is the home of the *mariachi* music. For a few *pesos* a young man can hire a group to serenade the girl he is going to marry. It is an old custom which some people like to keep.'

'It is a very nice custom,' she said. 'Do you know who hired them to come here?'

'Si.' Carlos sighed rather impatiently. 'It is Paco Colomo. He is going to be my son-in-law. I wish he had more care for his money.'

'Then they're serenading your daughter!' exclaimed Dawn. She felt disappointment wash over her and was at once irritated with herself. Why should she wish that the *mariachi* group had been hired to serenade herself?

'But of course, *señorita*. You know of someone else here who is getting married?' said Carlos dryly, and swung open the front door for her to enter, and after a brief hesitation she entered once again the cool airiness of the hallway. 'Señor Suarez says for you to wait here. He will not be long,' said Carlos. 'Please take your seat at the table.'

He led the way round the pool to the end of the hall where a small table was set with glinting silver ware. He pulled out a chair for her.

'Thank you, but I won't sit down yet,' said Dawn.

'As you wish, *señorita*,' he said politely. 'You would like another drink while you wait?'

Did he know what had happened to her first drink? Had he been watching through the curving leaves of the palm trees? Perhaps he had had to collect up broken glass. His dark eyes told her nothing as usual.

'No, thanks,' she muttered, and he nodded and went away through the usual archway.

Alone, Dawn wandered towards the pool again. She supposed Sebastian had gone upstairs to change his shirt. Standing on the edge of the pool watching the reflections of light dapple its green darkness, she recalled her recent behaviour with regret. She wouldn't be at all surprised if he withdrew his offer to marry her now and showed her the door. And who could blame him? No man would willingly marry a woman who appeared to be so shrewish.

But she wasn't normally like that. She had never deliberately hurt anyone in her life, had tended to be more gentle than tough. Then why did she react so violently to Sebastian? What made her so vulnerable to everything he did and said?

The sound of footsteps on the spiral staircase made her turn round. He came down into the hall, saw her and stopped. Across the winking pool they stared at each other. He had changed into a more conventional shirt, still white and still open at the neck, but somehow its businesslike plainness after the other more flamboyant one seemed an expression of a severe, cold mood.

Impulsively she moved towards him, walking swiftly round the pool until she was right up to him, not knowing what she was going to say but wanting to show him in some way that she regretted what she had done.

'I ... I ... hope the lemonade didn't damage your beautiful shirt,' she managed to say at last, although she couldn't look up and meet his eyes.

'I thought you'd gone for good that time,' he replied dryly. 'No, the shirt isn't damaged, but I am.'

She looked up then in surprise and gasped in consternation when she saw a strip of sticking plaster slanting across his left cheek.

'Oh, what happened?' she whispered. Her hand went up of its own accord as if to touch his cheek, then she withdrew it quickly when she saw the cold hostility in his eyes.

'Ice sometimes has sharp corners,' he remarked. 'At least, I think it was ice and not glass which cut my face.'

Glass? She remembered tossing her lemonade glass aside. Surely she hadn't thrown it at him? But suddenly strange feelings were welling up inside her which couldn't be controlled. Her legs went shaky and she swayed towards him, her hands going out to grasp his arms. Her eyes closed and she leaned her head against his chest.

'I'm sorry, I'm sorry, I'm so sorry,' she whispered. 'I didn't mean to hurt you.'

She waited for his arms to come round her and hold her close. She *ached* for them to hold her and was no longer afraid of the effect a close embrace might have on her just as long as he showed her he had forgiven her.

But instead of that warmth and comfort she felt his hands hard on her shoulders, pushing her away from him. He held her at arm's length and studied her with cold eyes.

'I accept your apology,' he said coolly. 'But would you please sit down to eat now? Manuela gets very temperamental if the food she prepares is ruined because it can't be served as soon as it's ready.'

He stepped past her to the table and held out a chair for her. She had guessed he could be haughty when he wanted to be, but she hadn't reckoned on his cool indifference having such a shattering effect on herself. Nervously, like a schoolgirl who has been caught breaking a school rule, she took her seat. Sebastian waited politely behind her until she was settled and then walked round to sit opposite to her. By the steady mellow light of the tall candles on the table his face looked proud and inscrutable and for once, without humour, and she felt her heart sink.

Carlos appeared almost as soon as they had sat down. Firstly they ate *ceviche*, succulent pieces of seafood marinated in lime juice and seasoned with oil, onions, chilli and tomatoes. It was followed by fillet of beef served with fried beans and strips of green peppers all covered by a rich avocado sauce. Carlos poured a light sparkling wine into elegant silver goblets and Dawn was glad to drink it because it took the edge off her nervousness.

Sebastian made no effort to talk to her and she was silenced by his unapproachability. Even when Carlos brought a dessert of fresh fruit, dishes of shelled nuts, a pot of coffee and a bottle of liqueur, then left them, the silence between them continued, accentuated by the tinkle of the fountain in the pool and the far-off sound of the *mariachi* music-makers.

Dawn nibbled nuts, drank coffee, sipped liqueur and racked her brains for something to say, but couldn't find anything which wouldn't seem like an obvious attempt to remind him of his proposal of marriage.

'Is your sister like you?' he asked suddenly, startling her, and she looked up. He was leaning back in his chair and watching her.

'In appearance?' she asked.

'*Si*. That will do to start with,' he said, and raised his liqueur glass to his lips.

'She's taller than I am and her hair is the colour of ripe corn and her eyes are blue,' Dawn replied, an affectionate smile curving her mouth as she thought about Judy. 'When she was eighteen she won a beauty contest. Dad was very proud of her, especially when she went in for acting.'

'How old is she?'

'Twenty-four, two years older than I am.' She caught her lower lip between her lip as a longing to see Judy surged up in her. 'I wish I could find her,' she whispered.

Across the table his eyes met hers. By candlelight they seemed darker than usual.

'Now that I know what she looks like there does seem to be a strong possibility that she is with Roberto,' he admitted, and his mouth took on a wry twist. 'He's known to have a weakness for blondes. Each of his ex-wives was a blonde.'

'Wives?' she exclaimed.

'He has had three. Each one of them was a film starlet trying to make it to the top in films and each time Roberto was deceived, so he says, into believing he was loved for himself and not for what he could do to further their careers.' He gave her another sardonic glance. 'Would your sister try that line if she thought there was a chance? Would she offer herself to him in return for a leading part in one of his films?'

'I don't know,' Dawn muttered. She fiddled with her liqueur glass not daring to look at him because the question bothered her. It touched so closely on what she was intending to do, agree to marry him if he would help her to find her sister. 'She might if she was attracted to your half-brother,' she added hesitantly. 'What is he like?'

'Short, inclined to be fat, in his mid-forties and very temperamental, as artistic people often are. But he's a great movie director and that's why he's attractive to young actresses.' He lifted his liqueur glass, drained it and set it down. 'Have you ever wanted to be an actress?'

'No, never.' She shook her head and smiled in reminiscence of her father's teasing. 'Dad always said that the acting abilities of the Aylwins had been left out of me. I'm no good at pretending.'

'I see,' he said softly, and pushing back his chair rose to his feet. 'If you've finished eating, perhaps you'd like to sit beside the pool here for a while or go out on the terrace,' he added politely. 'I have some telephoning to do, so please excuse me.'

'But you said ... I mean ... don't you want to know what my decision is?' she faltered, also getting to her feet and going towards him.

'Decision?' he queried, with a lift of his eyebrows. 'What decision is that?'

'About marrying you. You said before dinner you would like to hear what it is.'

'And you threw the contents of your glass in my face and ran away,' Sebastian said dryly. 'An unusual way of rejecting a proposal of marriage, I must admit, but no doubt you meant it since you're no good at pretending.'

'I didn't do it for that reason,' she protested urgently.

'Then why did you do it?'

'I ... I ... oh, I don't know. You were so aggravating. You ... you made me feel very confused,' she admitted miserably. 'I'd ... decided that I would say yes and agree to marry you and then you seemed to have changed your mind about it and I wasn't sure....' She broke off, unable to explain any further, staring at him with wide glistening grey eyes. Half turned away from him, his hands thrust into his trouser pockets, he was frowning down at the pool. 'You have changed your mind, haven't you?' she whispered.

He turned his head slowly and stared at her with half-closed eyes.

'You say *I* make *you* feel confused,' he exclaimed. '*Por dios*, that is nothing compared to what *you* do to *me*!'

In one stride he was in front of her, his whole attitude so threatening that she backed off and collided with the table so that the dishes rattled and the cutlery tinkled.

'So, you are afraid I might strike you,' he jeered, his eyes narrowing unpleasantly, and then he shook his head slowly from side to side. 'No, I could never hit a woman. If you were a man, I would. I'd half throttle you for some of the things you have said to me. Or I would bloody your nose. Or split your lip,' he snarled softly, leaning towards her until all she could see was the gold-fire of his eyes blazing into hers. 'But you're not a man, you're a young woman, and you believe you can say and do what the hell you like and get away with it by saying you're confused, because I make you confused.'

'Well, you do ... you have,' she retorted defensively. 'By asking me to be your wife after telling someone else we're going to be married.'

'It was the only way I could think of to protect you,' he replied, then drew a sharp breath, half turned away from her and then swung back. 'Sergeant Moreles came here today to take you away for questioning.'

'Questioning? What about?'

'About your association with two young criminals who are wanted in the State of California for being involved in drug-peddling and in this country for smuggling drugs. *Si, señorita*, you do well to gasp and hold your hand to your mouth in consternation. You described your friends Farley and Brett very accurately to the Sergeant who took notes as a good policeman should and showed them to his lieutenant, who recognised the men from the descriptions. The names they had given you were aliases and somehow they must have managed to get tourist cards issued in those names to enable them to enter the country again without being spotted at the border. It was clever of them to travel with you in a car hired in your name. You look and behave innocently.' He paused and gave her a hard searching look. 'But the lieutenant of police is suspicious of you. He believes you might be an accomplice and that under a certain sort of questioning you might break down and tell him where the criminals have gone.'

'But I'm not their accomplice,' she exclaimed. 'I ... I know nothing about them.'

'That is what I told Sergeant Moreles,' he said. 'How could you be without me knowing it, I said to him.' His mouth curved cynically. 'The young policeman is a romantic at heart and he lapped up the story I told him of how we had fallen madly in love with each other and intend to get married tomorrow in Guadalajara, and off he went back to the lieutenant.' He shrugged his shoulders and made a repudiating gesture with his hand. 'I regret that my intervention on your behalf has made you feel confused,' he went on dryly. 'And I have to admit I was in the process of changing my mind and withdrawing my proposal. Why the hell should I offer to bestow my name and worldly goods on an ungrateful, sharp-tongued little bitch just to get her out of the mess she's got herself into? That's what I was thinking while I waited for you to join me for dinner. Then you seemed to take matters into your own hands,' he touched the plaster on his cheek, 'and saved me the trouble. Carlos will drive you into Manzanillo tomorrow morning and leave you there,' he added coldly. 'I'm sure you'll manage very well without my help, since it only confused you.' The words had a sharp edge to them. '*Buenas noches, señorita.*'

Dawn couldn't have felt more stunned if he had struck her. In stupefied silence she watched him walk away round the pool and disappear through an archway. Then slowly she sank into a chair at the table. Head resting on her hands, she thought back over all that had happened since she had first met Farley at the film studios. In the light of what Sebastian had just told her she could understand now the strange behaviour of Farley and Brett on the beach the other afternoon.

When she had gone to find Farley to tell him that her sister wasn't in this house she had surprised him and

Brett with some of their drug-smuggling, drug-taking friends. They hadn't expected to see her again, would have moved on in the hired car without her while she was being reunited with her sister. But since she had turned up at an awkward moment, in the way of their kind, they had tried to make her one of them by forcing her to take a drug. And when she had refused they had tried to get rid of her. Amoral, utterly unprincipled, they had tried to drown her, and had nearly succeeded.

Dawn sat for a long time at the table, moving only when Carlos came to clear it. His dark unwinking eyes studied her closely, noting perhaps the marks of dried tears on her cheeks.

'You tired, *señorita*. You go to bed,' he urged quietly as he might have spoken to his daughter, and for the first time she saw him for what he was, not a close-mouthed, sharp-eyed watchdog, set by his employer to watch every move she made and prevent her from leaving the house, but a kindly middle-aged fatherly man.

'It doesn't seem long since I got up. I slept until noon,' she said.

'I know, but you have been ill and it isn't long since you nearly drowned,' he said. 'You need sleep and rest to make you better, give you strength.'

He was right. She was going to need all her strength tomorrow now that Sebastian had withdrawn his protection and help. So she smiled and nodded.

'*Buenas noches*, Carlos, *y muchas gracias*—for ... for ... everything.'

Tears brimmed again in her eyes and turning quickly she sped with a rustle of silk and the whisper of rope-soled sandals towards the staircase.

CHAPTER FOUR

SHE went to bed and surprisingly fell asleep straight away, worn out both emotionally and physically. But she slept barely a couple of hours, coming awake moaning and sweating, disturbed by a nightmare about drowning. It was a relief to open her eyes and to find she was still in the comfortable bed and for a while she lay bathed in sweat and entangled in sheets, blinking at the dim light which slanted in through the archway of the room from the hallway, showing up shapes of furniture, glinting on the glass of pictures hanging on the wall, casting weird shadows.

With a sigh of contentment because she was still in that luxurious haven, the gilded cage which had been built for a beautiful talented woman who had given up everything to live with the man she had loved, Dawn turned on to her other side. And then she remembered. Tomorrow she would have to leave. Tomorrow the door of the cage would be set wide and she would be free to fly away as she had been wanting to do. She would be helped on her way. She would be taken to Manzanillo.

But what would she do when she got there? To go to the police as she had once planned would be to walk right into trouble. A chill of dismay swept through her as she recalled reading in newspapers about innocent travellers going abroad and being arrested by foreign police because drugs had been found in their luggage, put there by smugglers. She couldn't go to the police for help because they would hold her for questioning and Sebastian would do nothing to help her. She had forfeited his help by her own wilful behaviour.

With a groan she turned over on to her other side. Muffled by the sheets, she could hear the sound of *mariachi* music, still being played, a haunting, insistent serenade designed to titillate the mind as well as the senses, to fuse them together creating a yearning to be loved and to love in return.

With her hands over her ears she tried to shut out the message of the music and her thoughts turned again inevitably to Sebastian, remembering how his kisses had lit so easily the flame of desire in her. He had said he wanted her, had offered to marry her, but in the end he had rejected her before she had had a chance to put into words her acceptance of his proposal.

How angry he had been—and who could blame him after the way she had behaved? Lying there now, dry-eyed, staring at the archway of light, Dawn could see quite clearly why she had been confused. Her mind had been speaking with a different language from that of her body. Her mind had said that marriage to him was crazy and she didn't have to go through with it. But her body had said she wanted him just as much as he wanted her, and it was still saying it.

She wanted to be with him now and make love with him in the warm tropical night while the bitter-sweet music outside unified mind and body, making of them a gift of love. A hot surge of excitement pulsed through her and an idea flashed into her mind, shocking her with its suggestiveness so that she rolled over hands clutching her head, her eyes tightly closed as she tried to blot it out. How could she go and offer herself to him now? He would think she was doing it because she was afraid of what was going to happen to her after she had been taken to Manzanillo tomorrow.

The music stopped. All was quiet; she couldn't even

hear the surf booming on the rocks below the terrace. Now perhaps she would go to sleep again. But light still slanted into the room, and although it was diffused it was enough to keep her awake now that the music had stopped. She had always preferred to sleep in a room that was completely dark.

Perhaps the light had been left on by accident. If she could find the switch and put it off she would go to sleep more quickly. Sitting up, she switched on the lamp by the bedside and slid from the bed. Moving silently on bare feet, she went through the archway on to the gallery overlooking the hall. To her surprise there was no light on in the hall, but light was shafting out of the room next to hers.

On tiptoe she walked carefully along the gallery and peeped into the next room. Mellow golden light from a bedside lamp slanted on to the bed and burnished the sun-bronzed bare skin of the back and shoulders of the man who was lying there on his stomach, only his legs and hips covered by the sheet. Sebastian had apparently fallen asleep without switching off his lamp.

Drawn into the room by the sight of gleaming skin and tousled black hair, Dawn walked as if in her sleep right up to the bed and looked down at him. His face was turned away from her and from the light. As she stared she felt again that hot surge of excitement and longed to thrust her hands into the tangle of his hair, to wake him and plead with him to let her stay with him and be married to him.

The longing was strong enough to send her to her knees beside the bed. All sensible thought in abeyance, completely at the mercy of her desires, she reached out a hand and touched his back, just below the top of the spine. Hardly had her fingers felt the supple smoothness of his skin than she snatched them back. What was she doing? Supposing he woke up? What would he say to her? What would he do?

Again imagining what he might do, she felt desire flame through her and again her hand reached out. Slowly, the fingers stroking and cosseting, greedily her hand moved to the broad nape of his neck beneath the clustering black hair before thrusting into the curls which as if they had a life of their own coiled about her fingers trapping them. Her breathing quickened and the nerves in her stomach fluttered. It was no use. She could no longer resist the desire to lie down beside him and wind her arms about him. . . .

Sebastian moved his head, twisting it on the pillow. Once more she snatched her hand back and knelt there, silent except for her quick shallow breaths, her eyes wide and her heart racing. He sighed, muttered something, but didn't move again, and she took one long breath, not sure whether she was relieved or disappointed. Then common sense came back. She had come in here to switch the light off, so she had better do that right now, and go back to her own bed, quickly before she was tempted again to slide into his bed and fondle him until he awoke.

She raised her hand to the lamp, not looking at what she was doing. Her hand collided with the bedside telephone, knocking off the receiver. Clattering loudly enough to wake the whole household, or so it seemed to Dawn, it fell to the floor with a bump and stayed there, its wire trailing over the edge of the table, and the high-pitched dialling tone seeming to fill the room with its sound.

Still on her knees, petrified by the result of her own clumsiness, Dawn watched Sebastian heave over on to his right side so that he was facing her. A frown drew his shapely eyebrows together and his eyelids lifted. Their clarity hazed with sleep, the golden eyes looked right at her before the thick fringes of lashes dropped again. The frown cleared, he settled his head more comfortably on the pillow and seemed to sleep heavily.

Dawn waited, looking down at the dark eagle-like profile of his face set off by the white sheen of the pillow. In sleep he looked more aloof and more proud than usual and she wondered how she had dared to say the things she had to him; how she had dared throw lemonade in his face. The sticking plaster which still slanted across his cheekbone gleamed lividly in the lamplight, reminding her that she had only herself to blame for his withdrawal of help. In return for his generosity she had given him only hard words and a gash on his cheek.

Moving with caution this time, she lifted the telephone receiver and replaced it with as little noise as possible. Then she raised her hand to the switch below the lamp's bulb, beneath the shade. Click, it was off, and the room was shrouded in intimate dimness, saved from being completely dark by the light which slanted into it from her room.

Dawn put a hand on the edge of the bed to steady herself before rising to her feet and gasped loudly when hard sinewy fingers closed round her wrist and Sebastian lunged up from the bed, a dark shape in the dimness, his eyes and the medallion on his chest glinting as they reflected the small amount of light.

'Surely you're not going without what you came for,' he whispered derisively, and his breath, warm and sweet with the *tequila* and wine he had drunk, drifted across her lips and nostrils, revealing how dangerously close he was to her. The heat of his body beat out to her temptingly and she tried to move away.

'I didn't come for anything,' she retorted. 'I wanted to switch off the light, that's all. The glow from it was shinning right into my bedroom and keeping me awake.'

'I don't believe you,' he scoffed.

'It's true,' she protested shakily.

'Then why did you touch me?'

'Please let me go,' she muttered. Now that he was fully awake and threatening she was in retreat again. She tried to pull her wrist free, but at once his fingers entwined with hers as they had done the morning they had met on the terrace and she was caught again in a wrestle to prove who was the stronger.

'It wasn't only the light which was keeping you awake, was it, *chiquita*?' he murmured. 'It was regret because I'd withdrawn my proposal of marriage. Right?'

'Yes,' she gasped. 'But how did you guess?'

'I've been going through a similar sort of hell myself,' he replied with a self-mocking laugh. 'So you want to marry me, hmmm?'

'Oh, yes, yes I do,' she sighed.

'Then show me that you do.' The softly-uttered suggestive words and the caress of his thumb against her wrist sent tingles of excitement racing through her.

'You mean....' she whispered, and broke off, the thunder of her heart loud in her ears.

'I mean show me that you want me.'

His voice was merely a breath in the night, tantalising and seductive, and her resistance was very low. Slowly she leaned forward and her lips found his mouth to press softly against its bold hard shape.

He didn't respond at first and aggravated by his coolness, she tried again, her lips pressing harder, her breasts, only half sheathed in silky chiffon and lace, pushing against the rib-ridged, hair-crisped hardness of his chest.

Still he remained unmoved and desperate to convince him that she was his for the taking if only he would respond, Dawn parted her lips so he could savour her mouth more intimately if he wished and placed her hands on the pulsing warmth of his body, her fingertips drifting shyly over his skin. At last, with a sound of surrender, half-gasp and half-groan, Sebastian pulled her down on to the bed with him to return her kiss with a passion which sent a thrill of exultation through her.

After that time passed in a haze of sweet voluptuousness as they lay close together, kissing and caressing, each learning by experiments how to please the other, and just when it seemed to Dawn that she was about to tip over the edge into a raging torrent of sensuousness from which there would be no return, Sebastian rolled away from her and sat up, his arms around his haunched knees, his head bent down to his knees as he took several long sighing breaths.

'So you have made your point, *chiquita*, I'm convinced,' he said huskily. 'And now you must go back to your bed.'

'Why?' she whispered, and was grateful for the darkness which hid the hot colour that seemed to sweep over her from head to foot at her own temerity.

'Why?' He turned to look at her and she saw the golden chain shimmer against his neck. 'Why?' He laughed, a short crack of amazed laughter. 'Because I don't sleep with a virgin unless I'm married to her, that's why,' he retorted.

'But....' She broke off as that tide of colour swept over her again and she was conscious of confusion again, disappointment mingling with a new feeling of respect for him.

'But what?' he prompted softly.

'Nothing,' she whispered.

'Listen, *querida*,' he murmured. 'I know what you would like to do and I would like it too. It would be very easy for us to anticipate our marriage night. But I don't want it to be that way between you and me. God knows it's hard for me to refuse you, but I think it would be in the interests of both of us if we don't. In the morning you might have changed your mind again or I might have changed mine. Let's leave the option open to the very last minute, shall we? Go to bed now and sleep, for we'll have to leave early in the morning to fly to Guadalajara.' He gave her a little push to help her on her way. '*Hasta luego, amada*, until later, my love,' he whispered.

Back in her own bed, with the light out and the velvet darkness hiding her shame at her own wantonness, Dawn lay with her eyes closed, but sleep seemed even further away. More than an hour ago she had lain there trying to blot from her mind the idea of going to Sebastian in the hopes of changing his mind, to persuade him to ask her to marry her again. Now it was done and she should be feeling happy and triumphant. But she didn't. Instead she felt more confused than ever, confused by his gentleness and his refusal to take what had been so freely offered.

She didn't fall asleep until dawn and was wakened almost immediately by the sound of dishes rattling on a tray. The touch of cool fingers on her shoulder brought her reluctantly out of oblivion. Her head was heavy and her eyelids seemed glued together as she sat up and replied to Manuela's cheerful *Buenos dias* with a muttered one of her own.

The fruit juice was icy and refreshing and the *tortillas*, light and fluffy, were drenched with honey. After a wash she went to the closet and took out the day dress made from ivory-coloured silk crêpe. It was simple in style with a low round neck gathered by a drawstring and a calf-length gypsy-style skirt. It fitted her perfectly. Sebastian had sized her up well, but he had forgotten about shoes and she could hardly wear rope-soled sandals with this elegant dress.

At that moment Manuela appeared and with a few gestures Dawn explained her predicament. The woman understood, nodded and left the room. Within a few minutes she was back, a pair of wedge-heeled white leather sandals in one hand and a pair of pale panty-hose wafting from the other. Dawn took the panty-hose gratefully and eased them on. Miraculously the sandals, merely narrow strips of leather attached to soles, fitted her.

'*Muchas gracias*, Manuela,' she said, and with a sudden exclamation the woman flung her arms about Dawn and kissed her heartily on both cheeks.

'*Vaya con Dios, señorita. Buena suerte*,' she whispered. Did Manuela know? Dawn wondered as she went along the gallery to the spiral staircase. Had Sebastian told Carlos and his wife that he and she were going to be married? Was that why the woman had blessed her and wished her luck?

Sebastian was in the hallway talking to Carlos. He was wearing a suit of pale fawn and a cream shirt which set off his dark colouring and she felt her pulse leap at the sight of him. Handsome and dynamic, he would soon be her husband. She could hardly believe it and for a moment she took fright. Then he turned and saw her, smiled and came towards her, a spray of red roses in his hand which he presented to her.

'What's this?' he asked, touching with a finger-tip the blue shadows beneath her eyes.

'I didn't sleep for a long while last night, and then I

was wakened so early,' she replied defensively.

'So you passed a night of doubt, did you?' he said with a mocking twist to his lips as he pretended he didn't know how she had spent part of the night and putting a hand beneath her elbow he turned her towards the front door. 'It's common enough, so I believe, for brides-to-be and bridegrooms-to-be to have last-minute doubts about the wisdom of their decision to get married. Do you like to fly?'

They were outside now, in the warm mistiness of the early morning, crossing a well kept lawn.

'I've only flown twice, once when I was a child from Ireland to Canada and then two weeks ago when I flew to Los Angeles,' she replied. The short grass was pearled with tiny glistening drops of sea-mist which wet her feet. Each globule of water quivered with rainbow colours as the sun came up swiftly from behind the mountains, flushing the eastern sky with rose-tinted golden light and glinting on the blue and white two-seater plane which was parked at one end of a landing strip in a flat cliff-top field adjacent to the lawn.

Sebastian swung open the door of the plane, then turned to help her up into the cockpit.

'You'll find flying in this a very different experience from flying in a jet-liner,' he said.

It all happened so quickly. There was a swift rush along the landing strip and then they were in the air, wobbling a little and rising slowly, only just clearing the tops of tall palms which edged the fields. And suddenly everything, the glittering white house, the deserted golden, palm-dotted beach, the other houses half-hidden in their trees tilted sideways as the plane turned and flew straight at the sun, which was now a ball of golden fire blazing down from between purple mountains.

Immediately below a river gushed in a foaming torrent between the walls of a steep gorge. The gorge widened out and the river widened with it, became a small lake, of silvery blue, caught in a bowl of biscuit-coloured rock. Then the lake had gone, sliding beneath as the plane turned to follow another river which wound like a bluish-green snake through a valley patterned with fields coloured brown and sand, flecked with the pale dusty green of sage bushes.

The plane lost height suddenly, seeming to fall towards the ground, then swept up again.

'What happened?' asked Dawn.

'We hit an air-pocket. It happens all the time when flying among the mountains.'

'I think I understand now why you like flying this way,' she said, glancing at him. 'It's something like being a bird.'

He flashed a surprised glance in her direction.

'It is, and you're right, that is why I like doing it. But there is something else which I do which comes closer to me being like a bird, and that is free-fall sky-diving.'

'You mean parachuting?'

'It's more than just jumping out of a plane and pulling the rip-cord. For the first few hundred feet you fall free without the help of the 'chute, and while you're falling you can do all sorts of acrobatics. It's like ballet in the sky. And the sensation is indescribable. There is a feeling of freedom you can experience no other way.'

'It must be very dangerous,' she commented.

'*Si*, it's dangerous, a flirtation with death. You can become so mesmerised by the feeling of freedom that you don't want to pull the rip-cord.'

'Has that happened to you?' she asked.

'Several times.' He laughed a short self-derisory laugh.

'I left pulling the cord until the very last minute, wanting to find out what it would be like if I didn't pull it, but in the end each time I lacked the courage to die.'

Dawn looked away down at the rugged dusty mountainside, seeing that shadow of the little plane black against the sand-coloured rock, and suddenly she was imagining him falling through space, turning over and over like a leaf in the wind until he hit that wall of rock and his splendid body was smashed to pieces.

'Oh no, please God, no!' she gasped, her hand to her mouth as sickness welled within her.

'*Que pasa?* What's the matter?' His voice was sharp.

'Nothing,' she muttered.

'Again?' he jeered.

'What's that patch of blue I can see in the distance?' she asked, ignoring his reminder of the previous night when she had given the same answer to a query of his.

'It's Lake Chapala, the largest lake in the country. We shall follow it to Guadalajara and fly in close over the Juancatlan Falls. They are Mexico's rivals to Niagara. And after that we'll be landing.'

Beneath the lake looked calm and blue between green hills. There were several villages scattered along its shores and Sebastian named them for her.

'Mostly they are holiday resorts,' he explained. 'Over there is Ajiijic. It's a centre for writers and painters. Many people from the film world come there to relax for a while. Roberto has a house there.'

As they flew over the small town Dawn looked down into it. Judy could be down there in one of those houses she could see half hidden by green foliage. She wished suddenly that she had a parachute and could jump out, float down into the town and begin her search. Then the houses had gone and looking ahead she could see water falling in a wide shining cascade over rock. Horseshoe-shaped, the great falls sent up a mist of white spume which glittered in the sunlight. Right over the twinkling effervescence Sebastian flew the plane before adjusting his headset and talking into the small microphone to the control tower at the airport, asking permission to land.

A few minutes later Guadalajara appeared, slanting towers of sun-glittered concrete and glass thrusting up from among the flat roofs of older buildings, all clustered together in a nest of green vegetation at the centre of a web of roadways.

The plane began to descend towards a crossroads of runways on a flat green field where other larger planes moved or were stationary, looking like great moths feeding on leaves. Dawn felt the nerves in her stomach twinge. But it wasn't fear of landing which caused the feeling. She was suffering from last-minute nerves. In a very short time she would be in that strange city, surrounded by strangers and being married to a stranger.

She couldn't go through with it. She turned to Sebastian to tell him, but he wasn't aware of her. He was too busy landing the plane. The wheel hit the runway and the plane taxied along with its engine clattering fussily. One hand to her mouth, Dawn stared out, hardly seeing the glitter of sunlight on other planes and vehicles, on the glass and concrete of the terminal buildings.

'Think of Judy,' she warned herself. 'Without his help you're not going to be able to find her. The price of his help is marriage, God knows why. If you don't marry him he'll do nothing. *Nothing*. If you tell him you can't marry him he'll just walk away from you, leave you to cope on your own, and you couldn't bear that, you know you couldn't because you....'

'*Bueno*. We are here.' Sebastian's voice was lazily

mocking as it cut across her thoughts and she realised the plane had stopped, was parked close to other similar small planes and the engine had been switched off. 'You are glad, perhaps, to be on the ground, safe and sound,' Sebastian went on with a touch of bitterness. 'Twice you have turned white and held your hand to your mouth as if to keep back sickness, once while we were over the mountains and once when we were landing. You didn't like the flying?'

The eagle glance of those golden eyes was too sharp, noticed too much. But she let him go on thinking she had been frightened of flying in the small plane because it wouldn't do for him to know the real reason for her nervousness. It wouldn't do for him to know she couldn't bear the thought of him hurtling through the air to his death or of him walking away from her, leaving her to fend for herself in this strange land. If she told him the truth he would want to know why she felt that way, and she couldn't tell him, not now, not yet, perhaps not ever.

So she shook her head slowly and negatively, not looking at him, and there was a brief tense silence.

'That is a pity,' he said in a low voice, then added sharply, 'But you will not try to stop me from flying?'

She looked at him then, quickly, in surprise. His face was taut and his eyes were cold and clear, almost cruel in the way he stared at her.

'Stop you? How could I stop you from doing something you want to do?' she exclaimed.

'In about forty-five minutes now you will be my wife and will have the right to try,' he said, and gave a short mirthless laugh. 'We shall both have lost some freedom, an aspect of our new relationship which I confess hadn't occurred to me before.' He gave her another hard stare. 'You still want to go through with it?'

She studied his face. He was having misgivings again and giving her a chance to refuse. Barely ten minutes ago she had turned to him to tell him she couldn't go through with it and then had found a reason why she wanted to marry him.

'I want to find my sister,' she said flatly, her gaze never wavering from his, and again there was a short tense silence. Then his mouth curved sardonically and his eyelids drooped over his eyes, hiding their gleam,

'But of course,' he drawled. 'How could I forget? Then let us go.'

There was a long cream limousine with a uniformed chauffeur waiting outside the terminal building to take them to the city centre. They sat one each side of the long wide back seat and Sebastian pointed out places of interest to her and talked generally in a cool aloof way about the city where he had grown up and had attended school and university.

'*Conocer a Guadalajara es amaria*—to know Guadalajara is to love her,' he said. And looking out at the shaded plazas, green parks, glittering fountains, elegant statues and sparkling buildings, Dawn could believe the statement.

The limousine passed along one end of the Plaza de Armas under the shadow of the Byzantine towers and domes of the Cathedral. People were strolling about the square under the shade of scattered trees or were sitting on benches in front of neat flower beds ablaze with the deep orange of marigolds, the scarlet of zinnias and the crimson and violet spikes of gladioli.

Leaving the square, the limousine drove down a wide tree-lined street of colonial buildings and stopped in front of one of them. Sebastian gave some instructions to the chauffeur, got out of the car and held the door for Dawn.

With a hand under her elbow he urged her towards the flight of steps which led up to the doorway of the building set under a triangular portico supported by long Doric pillars.

Almost at once, it seemed, a *mariachi* band started to play, trumpets blaring, guitars twanging and violins chirping. Glancing behind her, Dawn saw the players strolling by along the sidewalk, their silver-studded trousers and jackets winking in the sunlight, their voices raised in joyful rhythmical wedding music.

Even in the cool high-ceilinged room where she agreed to be Sebastian's wife and take him as her husband she could hear the beat of the music, and she was glad, for more than anything else it helped her to accept the brief obligatory civil ceremony as real.

Yet everything happened so smoothly that she had the oddest feeling that this strange marriage of hers had been planned for some time, as if Sebastian hadn't decided only the day before to marry a young woman he hardly knew. The feeling persisted and increased, making her silent and thoughtful as the limousine took them away down beautiful tree-lined boulevards.

'So it is done,' murmured Sebastian, shifting along the seat and taking her hand in his.

'Is . . . is this car yours?' she asked nervously.

'No, it belongs to a relative of mine,' he replied, and raised her hand to his lips. 'Tell me, Señora Suarez, how do you like your new name?'

'It will take some time to get used to it,' she replied breathlessly, withdrawing her hand from his and looking out of the window. 'Where are we going now?'

'To the house where my father's first wife lives,' he replied.

'She's still alive?' she gasped, turning to him.

'*Si*, she is still alive,' he answered, his eyes crinkling at the corner as he smiled tolerantly at her youthful surprise. 'But she is very frail now and not likely to live much longer. I want her to meet you, to show her that I have followed her advice and have at last got married. Why are you looking so amazed?'

'I ... I ... didn't think you ... or rather that she would have anything to do with you since you are the son of ... of....'

'Of the woman who broke up her marriage to my father?' he supplied dryly for her. 'But you see I am also his son and she loved him very much, and when my mother died Teresa became my mother, took me under her wing and looked after me. She is in fact the person I call Mother.' He slanted her a cold glance. 'You will be polite to her, *chiquita*,' he added sternly, 'for I care for her very much.'

'But won't she be surprised that you've married someone you've just met?' she exclaimed.

'I was hoping you would ask that,' he replied easily. 'She and her daughter, Raquel, my half-sister who lives with her, will believe I have known you longer than I have. I travel often to the States. They will believe I met you there.' He slid an arm behind her and she felt his fingers caress the curve where her neck joined her shoulder. 'You will follow my lead in this, please, *querida*?' he asked softly. 'To please an old lady?'

'Yes, but....' She got no further, for he bent quickly and kissed her and for a while all questions and suspicions were stifled by the sensual pleasure she found in that close embrace.

They kissed for a long time, not stirring away from each other until the car stopped. Moving as if in a trance, Dawn stepped out of the car into the quietness of the

courtyard where an old acacia tree grew, the delicate
tassels of its leaves fretting the white walls of the old
house with quivering fingers of shadow.

A door swung open and a woman stepped into the
courtyard. She was about fifty years of age, short and
rather plump. Her thick hair was plentifully streaked
with grey and her long oval face held a hint of sadness.
From under heavy drooping lids her dark eyes lit up
briefly with pleasure as she moved towards Sebastian to
embrace him. She hugged him and kissed him on both
cheeks. But that gleam had gone when she turned to look
at Dawn and considered her curiously. Then the woman
spoke quickly, almost passionately in Spanish, gesturing
towards Dawn with strangely graceful hands for one so
short and squat.

'This is my half-sister, Raquel Suarez,' Sebastian said to
Dawn with a smile. 'She thinks your colouring is unusual
and she would like to paint your portrait.'

'My portrait?' exclaimed Dawn.

'Si, si.' Raquel was nodding and her wide broad-lipped
mouth almost smiled. 'Forgive me,' she said in heavily
accented English. 'I do not greet you properly. You are
most welcome here, little-half-sister-in-law.' She moved
forward and kissed Dawn on both cheeks. 'You'll let me
paint your portrait?' she asked. 'I am a very good artist.
You will find my work all over Mexico.' She swung back
to Sebastian and gestured appealingly. 'You'll let her stay
here with me while it is done?' she demanded.

'Perhaps,' he replied with his taunting smile. 'It will
depend on what you can tell me about Roberto.'

'Roberto!' exclaimed Raquel, and went off into another spate of Spanish as they all walked towards the
door of the house. Sebastian slanted a derisive glance at
Dawn.

'As you can guess, there's no love lost between her and her brother,' he murmured. 'But be patient. In a while she'll get round to telling us where he is, because he writes and phones her all the time to make sure she knows what he's doing. She's his best publicity agent and tells everyone else what he is doing.'

After the light open airiness of the unusual house on the coast which had been built for Polly Moore, the old Colonial house where Teresa Suarez lived seemed very dark and formal with its cream walls, heavy dark furniture and red velvet curtains. Also the rooms had doors, big strong doors which gave the whole place a secretive atmosphere. Nothing was done openly here; whatever was done was done privately behind closed doors. From the hallway a wide staircase swept up to the upper floor and at the foot of the stairs Sebastian stopped and said,

'Raquel will look after you for a few minutes. I'm going to see Mother to prepare her to meet you. She isn't feeling too well this morning. You understand?'

Across the small space which separated them his eyes demanded her co-operation. As in the car when he had asked her to follow his lead Dawn felt a stirring of rebellion. It seemed there was much more to being married to him than she had ever anticipated. He expected her to obey him without question, and her freedom-loving spirit was objecting already to being taken for granted. Then she felt a hand on her arm. Raquel said,

'Come and see my studio,'

And so the spurt of rebellion was quelled and turning she went with Raquel along a passage and into a high wide room, full of odd pieces of furniture, easels and canvases. Big windows let in clear northern light and gave a view of a harsh bold landscape of sunlit mountains beyond the limits of the city. Almost before she had realised it Dawn was sitting on the edge of a chair upholstered in dark red velvet, her gaze steady on a corner of the room at which Raquel had told her to look, and Raquel was seated on a high stool and was sketching rapidly on a sketching pad.

'You are very pretty in a wild shy way and there is innocence in the lift of your chin and the slender bones of your throat. I can see your attraction for Sebastian and I know why he has married you. You will suit his purpose very well.'

'Purpose? What purpose?' exclaimed Dawn, turning her head sharply to look at the artist.

'Ah no, *querida*, do not look at me. Eyes on the corner, please,' said Raquel sharply.

'But you said....'

'I spoke carelessly, I often do,' replied Raquel. 'I meant only that since it is necessary for Sebastian to have a wife it is best that he should marry an unknown, innocent girl like you, quietly without publicity.'

Dawn, keeping her eyes steady in that corner, licked her suddenly dry lips.

'Why is it necessary for Sebastian to get married?' she asked stiffly.

'He has not told you?' said Raquel. 'Ah, then it isn't for me to say.' She made a few more strokes on her sketching pad, then said, 'A warning to you. My mother is very religious. To her way of thinking all marriages are made in heaven. She won't accept that you and Sebastian are really married until there is a church ceremony, even though the only ceremony recognised by the state is the civil one. Sebastian has told you about her, perhaps?'

'Only a little,' answered Dawn, uncomfortably wishing he had told her more.

'She refused to give Papa a divorce at first,' Raquel went on slowly. 'Only when she heard that Sebastian was going to be born did she agree, because she couldn't bear the thought of him being illegitimate just because she was too stubborn to give up her married status. I remember at the time she spent many hours in prayer, asking for guidance.' Raquel's voice shook a little. 'She loved Papa very much even though he didn't return her love, and she loves Sebastian because he is, of all Papa's children, the most like him.'

'Not in every way, I hope,' said Dawn, thinking that if Sebastian was like his father the time would come when he would want to end their marriage because he had found someone younger and prettier that he preferred to live with. Then she wondered why she should be worried on that count. Her strange marriage wasn't based on love but on mutual physical desire and had been brought about by blackmail, so why expect it to last?

'No, not in every way,' said Raquel. 'In looks very much so, except for the eyes. But like Papa he is bold, determined to have his own way, ambitious and clever. But then....' Raquel broke off and Dawn managed to send a sidelong glance in her direction. The artist was frowning a little and had paused in her sketching. 'I think,' she went on, 'there is a depth of compassion in Sebastian which Papa didn't have, an empathy for people less fortunate than himself, which is why he is more popular and successful as a politician than Papa ever was.'

Dawn showed her bewilderment. She couldn't help it, and yet, mindful of Sebastian's warning that Raquel probably believed he had known his new wife longer than he had, she didn't like to say she'd had no idea Sebastian was involved in politics.

'But I thought—I had the impression that Sebastian's father was in business of some sort,' she said.

'That is true. He was in many businesses. He had a genius for making money. He was in many things, producing cotton, vegetable oils, growing wheat and financing films. He was a millionaire by the time he was thirty-five. At forty-five he decided to take an interest in the government of this state. He had everything going for him, then he met and fell in love with Polly Moore when he was on a visit to Hollywood.' The bitterness in Raquel's voice when she spoke the name of Sebastian's mother made Dawn venture another sidelong glance in her direction.

'And did that make him change his mind?' she asked. 'About becoming involved in government, I mean?'

'No, but his illegal liaison with her turned the members of the party against him and he didn't realise his ambition. The people here, as anywhere else in the world, like their representatives to be respectable in their private lives. That is why....' She broke off and again Dawn glanced at her. Raquel was frowning and biting her lip.

'That is why what?' Dawn prompted.

'Ah, I talk too much,' said Raquel lightly, and with a few more strokes seemed to finish the sketch, for she held it at arm's length and studied it with half-closed eyes, 'You make a good model and I'm sure you'll make Sebastian a good wife and that the members of the party will be willing to have him as a candidate for the next election when they realise he has married a pretty young woman and is ready to settle down.'

'Election for what?' asked Dawn cautiously.

'The state legislative assembly. Sebastian has been a member of it for the past three years. He studied political theory at university and passed his exams brilliantly. A great future is predicted for him. But he must have told you about his ambitions.'

'I ... I'd forgotten,' muttered Dawn.

'How wonderful to be young like you and so much in love that you don't care what your husband does,' sighed Raquel wistfully. 'Sebastian is lucky to have met you, and I know when his colleagues meet you they are going to forget all those ugly rumours about him.'

'What ugly rumours? Raquel, you've got to tell me,' Dawn said urgently, leaning forward, and the older woman looked very worried.

'If I do, you promise you won't let what I've told you come between you and Sebastian?' she pleaded. 'They are, after all, only rumours, no truth in them at all, but if he hasn't told you himself he'll be angry if he finds out you heard about them from me.'

'I can't promise that they won't come between us until I know what they're about, can I?' argued Dawn.

'No, I suppose you can't,' agreed Raquel, her face creased into lines of anxiety, and for the first time she showed her age and Dawn saw her for what she was, a rather lonely middle-aged woman who sometimes let her tongue run away with her when she found someone to talk to.

'And surely it's better for me to learn the story from you than from someone else,' Dawn went on urgently, 'someone who isn't as fond of Sebastian as you are and who doesn't have his interests at heart like you ... and I have.'

'Si, you are right.' Raquel's face cleared and she smiled slightly. 'Then I'll tell you.' She paused and licked her lips and gave Dawn a sidelong wary glance. 'It is difficult for me to know how to put this. Sebastian has never been much interested in the idea of marriage, but that hasn't meant that he has been celibate. Do you understand?'

Dawn nodded. 'You mean that he has had lovers?' she said, and watched the red colour run up from Raquel's neck to spread across her olive-tinted face.

'*Si*, that is what I mean.' Raquel laughed a little self-mockingly. 'I forget that your generation is much more frank about such subjects than mine ever was. Sebastian has had lovers, as you say.'

'And the rumours you talk of have been about them?' exclaimed Dawn.

'*Si*. Not about the girls he used to know before he was elected to the legislature but about his close friendship with the wife of one of the other politicians.'

'Oh,' said Dawn. 'I see. How very foolish of him!'

'That is what Mama said to him when she heard about the rumours, and she suggested that the only way he could put a stop to the gossip would be to marry some nice young woman....'

'Preferably an innocent virgin,' murmured Dawn under her breath, her eyes wide and unseeing as she looked out of the window, beyond Raquel to the mountains. Then realising that Raquel was staring at her in puzzlement she turned and smiled at her. 'It was of course good advice,' she said. 'And I'm glad you've told me. I'll be forearmed now if anyone is so unpleasant as to suggest that Sebastian has married me just to cover up the affair he's been having with the wife of a colleague.'

'And you won't let it alter your feelings for him?' Raquel said anxiously. 'I can see you're very much in love with him.'

'Can you?' Dawn was disturbed. 'How?'

'The way you were looking at him in the courtyard when I opened the door.' Raquel put the sketching block aside and slid off the stool. 'You looked as if you had just had a glimpse of heaven.'

Because I'd just been kissed very thoroughly by a master at the art, thought Dawn miserably.

'But then I expect to be loved in return by Sebastian would be a little like being in heaven,' added Raquel wistfully. 'I can only guess, of course, because I've never been in love and no man has ever been in love with me. But come, it's time for lunch. Consuelo, our cook, has made Sebastian's favourite food because she knew he was coming today. It will be a quiet way to celebrate your marriage, but with Mama not being well I'm sure you'll forgive us.'

Although there were only three of them eating in the formal dining room at a shining table set with crisp white lace mats and shining silver cutlery it was a merry party, because Sebastian and Raquel seemed to share the same sense of humour, and for a while Dawn forgot the suspicions Raquel's remarks had roused in laughter.

Then somehow Raquel was talking about Roberto and she remembered she had married Sebastian because he had said if she did he would help her find her sister.

'Roberto is filming on location near Durango,' Raquel said.

'*Dios!*' groaned Sebastian, his hand to his forehead in mock dismay. 'Not another Western!' And he and Raquel both burst out laughing while Dawn stared at them completely mystified.

'You must excuse us,' said Raquel in her kindly way, turning to Dawn. 'But Roberto has always had a passion for Western stories and films. As a boy and a young man he always identified with the strong silent gunslinging hero who puts everything right for the poor struggling widow of a rancher and then rides off into the sunset. But since there was never any possibility of him ever acting that part in a film he decided to make such a film, and that was how he started on his career as a movie director. *Si*, it's another Western with a strong Mexico bias, but with a *gringa* heroine.'

'A blonde, of course,' suggested Sebastian smoothly, finishing the last of his wine and then wiping his mouth on a stark white linen serviette.

'Of course,' said Raquel with a sigh. 'Could there be another other sort of heroine?'

'Has he fallen in love with her yet?' asked Sebastian dryly.

'No, I don't think so. He says only that he feels she is very suitable in the part.'

Across the table Dawn's eyes sought Sebastian's. She longed to ask if Raquel knew the name of the blonde actress. But Sebastian, guessing what she wanted to know, shook his head slowly, almost imperceptibly from side to side. Apparently he thought it wasn't necessary for Raquel to know about Judy. So she said instead,

'Where is Durango?'

'North of here. So many films have been made there that it's known as Little Hollywood,' said Raquel enthusiastically. 'There's a great variety of scenery around there—mountains, canyons, plains and plenty of horses and cattle, for it is ranching country. The climate provides the special brilliance of light which makes the shooting of exterior scenes a movie-maker's delight. Many well-known films have been shot there, including some of John Wayne's. You should take Dawn there, Sebastian.'

'Maybe I shall, after we've had our honeymoon,' he said quietly, but there was nothing quiet about the glance he gave Dawn. Then the moment had passed and he was pushing back his chair. 'Please tell Consuelo she surpassed herself today. It was an excellent meal,' he said. 'I'll take Dawn to see Mother now.' He looked at Dawn again. 'It won't take long, *querida*. She is too short of breath to talk much and can't speak English anyway.'

The interview lasted only ten minutes. The old lady, although obviously ill, was sitting straight on a chair beside a window in a big bedroom which overlooked the street and she was watching the traffic go by. She wore a plain black dress and a gold crucifix glinted on her narrow chest. Her white hair was cut short and it contrasted starkly with her walnut-coloured skin and deep black eyes.

She studied Dawn gravely, then raised her thin arms in welcome. Responding to the push in the small of her back which Sebastian gave her Dawn bent forward to put her arms round the slight shoulders and kissed the papery wrinkled cheeks. As she straightened up Teresa touched a strand of the pale blonde hair which lay on her shoulder and whispered something in her asthmatic voice to Sebastian.

'What is she saying?' asked Dawn. 'Is it about me?'

'*Si*.' Amusement rippled through his voice as he translated. 'She says she hopes you'll be a good wife to me and make me always welcome in your bed.' He smiled tauntingly and added softly, 'I hope you will, too.'

He said a few more words to the old lady, raised her hand to his lips, told Dawn to say goodbye to her in Spanish and then they left the room. Raquel was waiting in the hallway to say goodbye and soon they were in the back seat of Teresa Suarez's limousine being driven along the sunny streets.

'Where are we going now?' Dawn asked.

'To the airport, to fly to the coast,' Sebastian replied.

'Couldn't we go to Durango?' she said, turning to him

impulsively. 'Now, this afternoon, to find your half-brother. Judy could be the blonde actress in his new film and you said you would help me find her if I married you. Well, we're married now....'

'*Si*, we're married now,' he interrupted her softly. He touched her throat and his thumb caressed the tender skin beneath her ear. His eyes darkened as he leaned towards her. 'But I would like to consummate the marriage before we go to Durango,' he added, and his lips touched hers in a tantalising feather-like kiss.

'We ... we could do that in Durango,' she suggested shyly, her heart beating wildly.

'In some hotel?' he queried. 'Ah, no, *querida*. It will be done in a place where we shall be alone.' His fingers trailed possessively down her throat and slid insinuatingly under the low gathered neckline of her dress. 'Where no one will be worried if we choose to stay upstairs all day in my room or yours. Or if we decided to make love beside the pool or in the *salón*. Where we'll be free to express what we feel for each other whenever we want to.' He put his head close to hers to whisper in her ear and the musky fragrance of his hair and skin acted like a drug on her mind, making it spin until all thought of resistance vanished. 'I want you, *chiquita*, and it's getting harder by the minute to have to wait before we can be together, be as one.'

Oh, it was impossible to resist an appeal like that when all her senses were clamouring to do just as he had suggested, to be united with him in a joyous natural mating, so putting her arms about him she turned her lips to his and once more let his kiss take her close to heaven.

'From your response I gather that you agree with me, pretty bird, and would like to return to *la casa chica*,' he murmured huskily against her cheek, and too breathless to speak, Dawn nodded, and had no recollection afterwards of the rest of the journey to the airport.

The flight back to the coast also had a dreamlike quality. Beneath the wings of the little aircraft the sun-baked land shimmered in the afternoon heat and ahead of them the hot blue sky was split by the jagged edges of the biscuit-coloured mountains. Then they were in the cool blue shadows of the gorge with the fast river foaming and twinkling in its rush to the sea. The gorge widened and there before them was the bright glitter of the sun on the blue ocean. The plane turned. A palm-shaded beach edged with white surf tilted skywards, and the green cliff-top rushed up to meet the plane. It landed and there sparkling white among drooping fringes of palms were the arches and domes of *la casa chica*, the gilded cage built for Polly Moore.

'Glad to be home?' asked Sebastian, sliding an arm about her waist, as they walked towards the house.

'Home? Is this where we're going to live always?' Dawn asked, and glanced up at him. The clean-cut angle of his jaw above the now opened collar of his cream shirt, the humorous curve to the corner of his mouth, the thrust of strong cheekbone through taut tanned skin, the glint of golden light between thick black lashes as he slanted a glance her way and the lifting of silver-threaded silky black curls away from his temple and brow, all made her weak suddenly with desire and she felt a new thrill pulse through her. This man was hers. In the eyes of the law of the land he was committed to share everything he had with her, to love and cherish her just as she was committed to him to do the same. The feeling of possessiveness was primitive and frightened her a little. She had always considered herself to be above and apart from such feelings. Her generation lived and let live, it didn't demand possession. It didn't take over.

'I like that *always*,' he murmured. 'It seems to indicate that you hope to live with me always. We shall live here as much as possible, but we'll also spend much time in Guadalajara. I have a large apartment there, but if you would prefer it we could have a house.' He laughed a little. 'Unlike other couples in the same situation we haven't discussed the mundane details associated with marriage, where to live, how many children. We just took a chance, jumped out, hand in hand, to fall free together....' He broke off and came to an abrupt stop as if he had walked into a glass door. They had come round the corner of the house and there on the driveway parked in front of the steps was a car, an elegant silvery-blue vehicle, shimmering in the sunlight.

Although his arm was still around her it lost its intimate possessive touch, became as stiff as a board. Dawn glanced at his face again. It was drawn into such an expression of bitterness that she could only exclaim urgently,

'Oh, what is it? What's wrong?'

His glance flicked down to her and his expression softened. His arms tightened briefly about her and then was gone. Raising his hand, he rubbed the knuckle of his forefinger along her chin in a simple heart-shaking caress.

'It seems we have visitors,' he said softly. A strange tautness came into his face, his eyes darkened with some barely suppressed emotion and he caught his breath in a short shaky sigh. 'I'm sorry, *querida*. It means a delay to what we planned to do. I have to ask you to be patient and help me entertain them.' He bent his head and touched her lips with his in a brief passionate kiss which made her sway where she stood and cling to him. Then taking her hand in his he drew her after him up the steps.

The door opened before he touched it and Carlos stood there.

'*Buenas tardes, señor y señora*,' he said in his expressionless way. 'Welcome home.'

'Thank you, Carlos,' said Sebastian, and continued in Spanish, obviously asking about the visitors.

The hallway was as usual, cool, silvery green, tinkling with the sound of falling water. Her hand still in Sebastian's grasp, Dawn listened to the exchange of question and answer between the two men, wishing she knew more Spanish, vowing that now she was married to a Mexican she was going to learn it. She watched their faces for some clue about the subject of their conversation, but learned nothing. They were both inscrutable.

'Our visitors are Armando Gonzales and his wife Micaela. He is a colleague of mine,' Sebastian said, turning to her. 'They don't know of our marriage, of course, so I'll go and tell them while you go upstairs to freshen up after your journey.' His voice was crisp and cool, issuing orders, expecting them to be carried out because now she was his wife, committed to helping him in his career to entertaining his guests. She felt again that little surge of rebellion, the natural reaction of a freedom-loving spirit to domination. She lifted her glance to him, opened her mouth to protest, and he smiled down at her a little sardonically, speaking before she was able to form her words.

'I would like you to look your best, *chiquita*, and to try and pretend a little that we have known each other longer than five days,' he said softly, then added tauntingly, 'And if you can't bring yourself to do it for me, remember Judy, and do it for her.'

CHAPTER FIVE

ARMANDO GONZALEZ was a broad-shouldered, thick-set man of about forty-eight years of age. His greying dark hair was cut short and brushed back neatly from a wide, low forehead. He wore gilt-rimmed spectacles and their flashing lenses made it difficult to judge both the colour of his eyes and their expression so that his fleshy, flat-nosed face had a bland inscrutable appearance. He was dressed in a well-cut lightweight grey suit, a crisp white shirt and grey tie. He looked and behaved like the politician he was, smooth and polite with just enough geniality in his manner to make him seem approachable and kindly.

His wife Micaela was beautiful, or at least Dawn thought she was. She was so beautiful and elegantly turned out that for the first few minutes after being introduced Dawn could only stare with wide eyes at the perfection of creamy skin, full passionate red lips, deep brown, heavy-lidded eyes and shining black hair, demurely parted in the middle and smoothed down straight on either side to curve over the ears back into a tight chignon at the nape of the neck. Micaela was wearing an expensively simple afternoon dress of rose pink cotton and the only jewellery she wore was pendant ear-rings so long as to almost touch her shoulders. Dawn guessed her age to be similar to Sebastian's.

After a quick assessing glance at Dawn from under discreetly shadowed eyelids Micaela smiled, showing perfect teeth, and to Dawn's surprise leaned forward to kiss her on both cheeks.

'Congratulations, I hope you will be very happy,' she

said in an attractive throaty voice, then looking past Dawn she said something to Sebastian in Spanish.

'You'll have to speak English, Micaela,' he said, looking up from the drink he was pouring for Armando. 'Dawn doesn't understand much Spanish yet.'

'Ah, forgive me,' said Micaela, turning back to Dawn and smiling again. 'I said only that Sebastian is fortunate to have found someone so pretty and innocent to be his wife. Come, sit beside me,' she added patting the grey velvet covering of the chaise-longue on which she was sitting, behaving as if she were the hostess in that house. 'I hope you and I are going to be good friends. Sebastian and I have known each other since our childhood. My family lived for a long time in the house next door to the house where Raquel Suarez still lives. Sebastian and I played often together when we were small. Didn't we, *querido*?' she called across to Sebastian, but he didn't seem to hear and was turning away to listen to something Armando was saying. Micaela's face changed suddenly, lost its brightness for a few seconds, showed fine lines of discontent drawn in about the corners of the mouth and a gleam of malice came and went in her velvety eyes. Then she smiled again and the impression was gone. 'Those two,' she said with an expressive gesture in the direction of Sebastian and Armando where they paced slowly beside the pool, taking sips from their glasses as they talked seriously, 'they talk nothing but politics when they meet.' She shrugged. 'Sebastian tells me you are from Canada. What part?'

Dawn answered her and much to her relief the conversation went on along less personal lines and she didn't have to say much because Micaela obviously liked talking, mostly about the travelling she had done. Dinner was served, again by the pool, and with his amiable smile Armando, sitting on her right, devoted his attention to Dawn, talking pleasantly and lightly and often with humour about his own country and its people.

'We Mexicans are a new race of people, historically speaking, with a very mixed heritage,' he said. 'Our paternal ancestors were Spanish Conquistadors who fathered us on the female descendants of the civilised people who had been living in this part of the world for thousands of years, the Aztecs, Mayans and Tlaxclans. You can see the mixed blood in Sebastian and me, even in Micaela, and we are very proud of it. Now there are traces of other origins in us French, German, Italian, Chinese, Negro....'

Only half listening to him, Dawn watched Micaela and Sebastian rise to their feet and leave the table to walk by the pool. After lingering for a few minutes to watch the fish they strolled away down the hall, Micaela doing all the talking and, by the time they reached the archway which led to the *salón* and went through it, Micaela's hand was through the crook of Sebastian's arm.

'You must excuse Micaela if she seems to have commandeered your husband.' Armando's voice was sharp with irony and Dawn gave him a startled glance. He was watching her through the haze of smoke which spiralled up from the fat cigar which he held between thick brown fingers. 'For the past year or so they have been having an affair which has come close to ruining his career as a politician. It's been a clever move on his part to marry you. Politically speaking a wife is a great asset. Shall we follow them on to the terrace?'

Standing up, he moved round to the back of her chair to ease it from under her as she stood up. Completely bewildered and out of her depth, Dawn turned rather blindly to walk down the hall to the *salón* and found her hand taken and her arm drawn through Armando's.

'We'll take our time,' he said. 'No need to appear too obvious or jealous.'

'But I don't understand,' Dawn blurted. 'If you know your wife is having an affair with another man how can you stay married to her?'

'Because it suits me to stay married to Micaela,' he replied smoothly. 'She's the daughter of our present Governor who has been very useful to me in the furtherance of my own career. I've no intention of divorcing her. At the moment she is caught up in a fantasy of romance. She was in love with Sebastian years ago, then she lost touch with him. He turned up in her life again when he was elected to the legislature three years ago. Let her have her little fling with her childhood sweetheart and now that he has had the good sense to take a wife of his own, no harm will come to anyone.'

Chilled to the marrow by his cold-blooded attitude, Dawn forced herself to continue to walk beside him. So everything Raquel had told her was true and not merely rumour. Sebastian had had, was still having and probably was going to continue to have an affair with the wife of a political colleague and he was going to use his own marriage to herself as a screen to hide that affair.

She was glad suddenly of the support of Armando's arm, for she felt very faint and sick as if someone had given her a blow to the stomach. *No harm will come to anyone.* Armando's cynicism appalled her. What about her? Wouldn't harm come to her? More than half in love already with Sebastian.... Her thoughts came to a screeching stop. Oh, God, what was happening to her? She must get out, fly away before she became entangled in the web of intrigue which was being spun about her by these worldly, sophisticated people. Hand to her mouth, she pulled her arm free and with a muttered excuse turned and hurried back down the long *salón* into the hall, up the spiral staircase and into the bedroom she had been using.

Finding she was shaking in every limb, she sat down on the side of the bed and took a deep breath to try and control herself. If only the room had a door with a lock and key so that she could be alone, completely alone to think. If only there was somewhere else she could go to escape from Sebastian, because she was sure that when Armando reported what had happened, Sebastian would come looking for her and using his expertise as a lover would try to obliterate all suspicions from her mind.

'Dawn? Where are you?'

Micaela's deep throaty voice sounded concerned and her high heels made clicking sounds on the polished wooden floor of the gallery. Springing to her feet, Dawn went over to the window of her room to stand there looking out with her hands pressed against her cheeks.

'Ah, there you are. Armando said he thought you were feeling a little sick.' Micaela advanced into the room. 'The food, perhaps? You are not yet used to our spicy sauces? Are you all right?'

'Yes, thank you.' Dawn swung round. 'It ... it's kind of you to come and ask.'

'I have really come to say *adios*. We are leaving now.' Micaela glanced round the room. 'What a pretty house this is,' she said on a sigh. 'This is the first time I have ever been in it. Sebastian has told me about it many times, of course, but somehow it has never been possible for him to invite me here. And now that I've come at last it has to be with Armando and I ... I ... find you here.' The full red lips twisted into a rueful smile. 'Strange to find a man's wife in the little house which is usually reserved for his mistress.'

Dawn gasped and her eyes went wide, but she couldn't think of anything to say, she wasn't used to dealing with malicious innuendo. Micaela frowned, obviously puzzled by her innocent, slightly shocked reaction.

'Of course, I had forgotten,' she apologised. 'You're not used to that custom.'

'What custom?'

'Why, the custom of a man having a mistress as well as a wife, of course. It still happens in this country. You know Sebastian and I fell in love with each other years ago.'

'Oh, really. Why didn't you marry?' Dawn tried to sound coolly interested.

'My father wouldn't let me marry him.' Micaela swung round to face Dawn. 'You wouldn't understand that, either, you who are so used to your freedom. He ... my father ... is a very proud man, proud of his lineage, on one side Spanish and on the other Aztec. He didn't like the idea of his only daughter marrying a man who was born on the wrong side of the blanket.'

'But Sebastian's birth was legitimised,' said Dawn.

'*After* he was born,' said Micaela softly. 'That was the bone which my proud father refused to swallow. And who was to know where Polly Moore came from? She was a jumped-up little nobody who had probably got her parts in films through distributing her favours to the men who could help her with her career. . . .'

'How cruel of your father to imply that!' exclaimed Dawn angrily.

'I thought so too, at the time, but then I was in love. I was sent away to school in Switzerland to be finished and polished.' Micaela's mouth took on a bitter twist. 'When I came back I was duly married to Armando.

And now. . . .' She shrugged and sighed and made a gesture with both hands. 'We are still in love, you know, Sebastian and I. It isn't over, our affair, and it never will be over. I thought you should know that. *Buenas noches*.'

She went from the room and again there was the sound of her heels clicking on the gallery floor, the sound of her voice calling over the gallery railing to someone who was in the hall.

Dawn stood a long time looking out at the stars, only moving when she heard other heavier footsteps coming along the gallery. Then turning quickly she whisked into the bathroom, shut the door and turned the key in the lock. Bending over the bath, she flicked both taps on. Water gushed out noisily. Impossible with that row going on to hear whether anyone called to her through the closed door or even turned the handle of the door. She had found the place where she could be alone to think, where she could escape from Sebastian.

When the bath was so full of water it was in danger of running over she turned off the taps and listened. There was no sound from the other side of the door, so she slipped off the green gown she was wearing and hung it carefully on a hook behind the door, stepped out of her underwear and got into the bath. There was so much water in it that her legs kept floating up and eventually she let some out.

Think. She had to think of a way out of this new predicament she was in. Oh, it was so easy now to see how she had been manipulated by Sebastian, taunted and tempted by him until she had agreed to marry him. But she couldn't do what he wanted her to do, not now, knowing about Micaela and him. With an indrawn breath of pain she remembered the expression on his face when he had seen the car belonging to the Gonzalez', the bitterness she had seen there. And yet only a few minutes before that there had been a closeness between them which had been more of the spirit than of the body and she had felt strongly that he was in love with her and she with him and that everything was going to be all right, would end happily.

But now she knew he wasn't in love with her. He was in love with Micaela, who was in love with him. They were lovers. That was what was hurting so much, stabbing through her like a knife. They had made love together in the same way that he was expecting to make love with her, now, tonight, because she was his wife! Oh, she couldn't do it. She couldn't, knowing about Micaela.

Knuckles rapped sharply on the bathroom door, startling her out of her uneasy thoughts.

'Who is it?' she called nervously.

'Me, your husband, *querida*,' Sebastian sounded amused. 'I'm glad to hear your voice and to know that you haven't drowned in the bathtub. You have been in there a long time. The Gonzalez' have gone and we are alone at last. I know you wish to be beautiful for me, but I'm getting impatient. I'll give you five more minutes and then....' He paused threateningly.

'What will you do?' she exclaimed, and stood up in the bath so quickly that the water slid from side to side.

'Break down the door, of course, snatch you up in my arms and carry you off to my bed,' he growled, but there was a ripple of laughter beneath the growl.

'Five minutes, then,' she called out, and grabbed a big towel from the rail. 'Where will you be?'

'Can't you guess?' he replied mockingly.

After that there was silence and she assumed he had gone, returning to his own room. She took her time over drying, letting the five minutes drag out to ten, thinking that if she didn't hurry he might fall asleep. One thing was sure, she wasn't going to his room tonight, not even to put out a light, and if he came looking for her and tried to make love to her she would just tell him that she couldn't, she wasn't in the mood, she had a headache, she felt sick—tell him anything to put him off. And she knew he would withdraw, for hadn't he once said there was no pleasure in making love to an unwilling woman?

When she was thoroughly dry she realised that she hadn't brought the nightgown with her into the bathroom, so she draped the big towel around her sarong-wise, unlocked the bathroom door, opened it and peered cautiously round the edge of it into the bedroom. The room was as she had left it, lit only by one lamp whose shaded light slanted across the silken sea-green sheen of the bed, showing it to be flat and uninhabited.

With a quick glance round the rest of the room to make sure no one was there, she went across to the bed, assuming that whoever had tidied the room and had made the bed that day had put the nightdress under one of the pillows. Bending over the bed, she pulled back the covers and slid her hands under each pillow in turn. There was no nightdress.

She straightened up, then let out a cry of fright and surprise when she felt hands, cool, lean and long-fingered, touch her shoulders and slide forward diagonally across her breasts to pull her back against a warm, bare masculine body.

'Forget the nightgown,' whispered Sebastian into her hair. 'You're not going to need it tonight. Nor will you need this.' And with slow caressing movements of his hands he smoothed the towel away from her and tossed it somewhere into the shadows.

'I ... thought you'd gone to bed,' she gasped, closing her eyes and willing herself to ignore the wantonness which was leaping through her at the feel of his muscular pulsing body pressed closely against her back and the delicate seductive touch of his fingertips as they caressed her.

'Without you?' he queried, and hands resting lightly on her waist turned her so that she faced him. In the lamplight his eyes were opaque under heavy lids as they studied her face. 'I couldn't,' he added softly. 'I want you too much.'

'Sebastian,' she said urgently, putting her hands behind her back and gripping them tightly together there because she had an overwhelming desire to touch him, to slide her hands about his waist and over the curve of his hips, but she mustn't, because it had to be said before those devastating fingers of his could find the hidden sensitive nerve-endings and light the flame which would run along the fuse and lead to an explosion of desire in her. 'There's something I must say to you.'

'Important?' he murmured.

'I think it is.'

'Are you going to say you want me very much too?' His voice was slightly muffled as he kissed her throat. 'Because if you aren't don't talk at all. There is a time for serious talk and a time for love-talk, and now is the time for love-talk....' He went off into Spanish as he gathered her against him, his hands stroking her back with long slow caresses until she was moulded so closely against him she caught her breath as excitement beat through her.

'I don't understand what you're saying.' It came out in a sort of gasping sigh, half protesting, half exulting as, suddenly beyond her control, her body arched against his.

'I'm saying only that I'm in love-desire and I can wait for you no longer,' he whispered breathlessly, and suddenly he lifted her and then somehow they were both lying on the bed, mouth to mouth, breast to breast. 'You are so small and pretty, *querida*,' he went on huskily, 'and I don't want to hurt you, but I don't think I can be gentle. . . .'

But by now Dawn didn't care what happened. All thought was in retreat before the strength of the life-force which was throbbing through her in answer to his demands. Holding him closely she whispered two of the few Spanish phrases which she knew and which came most closely to expressing how she was feeling,

'*De nada, el gusta es mio*. You're welcome, the pleasure is mine.'

And then it was as if a dam which had been holding back a torrent burst. His mouth was against hers bruisingly so that breathing was almost impossible, he pinned her with his weight against the bed and after that it was like drowning again as she was swept along on the tumultuous torrent of his desire for her. Yet through the painful bursting darkness she was aware suddenly of joy like a great flash of light exploding all about her. And afterwards there was a warm sensuous afterglow and the wetness of tears on her face and on his.

Curled up in his arms, her cheek against the smooth silky hardness of his shoulder, she fell asleep, motionless, lying in the kind of peace she hadn't known since childhood, and didn't wake for a long time.

When she did wake she felt different and for a while she lay with her eyes closed, wondering why she should feel that way, for she knew she was alone. No arms held her comfortingly and there was no smooth hardness of skin-sheathed muscle beneath her cheek.

It was full daylight, she could tell by the brightness, she could sense through her eyelids and she was still in the comfortable bed—she could tell by the silken feel of the sheets against her bare skin. But there was a difference. She was different. She was lighter than air, floating like a feather, happy because at last she knew what heaven was like.

She opened her eyes, saw the rumpled head-dented pillow beside her and the creased tangle of the sheet. Beyond the bed was a splash of green on the floor which was the towel Sebastian had taken from her. Then it all came flooding into her mind, the memory of what had happened, the pain and the ecstasy, the warmth and whispers of passion, and with a little groan of dismay she turned her head and buried her face in the pillow.

The slithering sound made by rope-soled sandals moving over the wood of the gallery floor meant that Manuela was coming. Dawn turned on to her back, making sure that she was covered by the sheet. The woman appeared in the archway carrying the breakfast tray which she set down on the bedside table. Her dark eyes slanted a sideways glance at Dawn and she smiled, just a little.

'Buenos dias, señora,' she said expressionlessly, and had whisked away out of the room before Dawn had time to remember the Spanish for 'where' so that she could ask where Sebastian was.

She couldn't help feeling disappointed because he hadn't stayed in her bed, she thought, as she slid off the bed and went to the closet to take out the silk dressing gown. But she supposed, with a new and disheartening cynicism, that having got what he wanted he had seen no reason to linger with her. And yet, yesterday, he had indicated that he would once they were alone, here in this house.

Perhaps he had felt unsatisfied. Perhaps he had found her too innocent. After all, if he were accustomed to making love with a knowledgeable sophisticated woman like Micaela.... Her hand shook suddenly so that she had to put down the glass of fruit juice which she had picked up from the tray. Sitting down on the side of the bed, she buried her face in her hands as she remembered how she had intended to refuse to let Sebastian make love to her last night because she couldn't bear the idea of doing it after what Micaela had told her.

How easily he had been able to defeat her intention. Once he had touched her she had been lost, betrayed by her foolish susceptible body. And that was how it was always going to be if she stayed here and lived with him. He was always going to be able to silence her with kisses and caresses, and all the time she would know that when he wasn't with her he would be with Micaela....

'*Qué pasa, chiquita?*' He had come into the room again without her hearing him, but she knew he was near this time because she could smell the sea on his skin. He had been out surfing while she had slept. But she didn't move her hands in case he saw the tears which had begun to brim in her eyes. 'Dawn, *querida*, look at me and tell me what is wrong?' he asked.

Then his strong fingers were round her wrists and he was forcing her hands away from her face. He was kneeling on the floor before her. His bare sun-tanned shoulders were damp and glittered here and there with drops of sea-water which dripped from his wet hair. The expression of tender mockery in his eyes as they looked right into hers made her long to fling herself against him and weep into his shoulder.

'Were you missing me a little?' he taunted softly,

wiping a tear from her eyelashes with a gentle forefinger. 'Were you worried when you awoke and found I had gone? I'm sorry I couldn't stay to kiss you awake. I had to go and answer the phone and then the sea and the surf called to me. But you see, I've come back to have breakfast with you and afterwards. . . .' He broke off and leaned forward, his eyes darkening with passion, his lips parting as they came closer to hers, his hands on her knees sliding up her thighs, slowly, suggestively.

'No, no!' she cried, turning her head away from him. 'I can't. I don't want to. Please, please don't make me!'

Sebastian's hands were suddenly still and she heard him draw his breath in sharply.

'This time it will be different, *querida*, I promise you. Last night was only the beginning. If I was a little rough it was because I wanted you so much. *Te quiero muchisimo.* I love and want you very much,' he whispered.

I love you. The words she, no better and no worse than any other young woman, had always hoped and longed to hear one day, and now she was hearing them and was finding it impossible to believe them.

'I wonder how often you've said that to a woman,' she said, and even to her own ears her voice sounded cold and light, almost mocking, and she felt a little surprised she had actually said them.

'*Como dice?* What did you say?' he demanded, his voice husky with disbelief.

She turned to look at him. He was still on his knees, but he wasn't touching her any more and had raised a hand to his forehead to wipe away some sea-water drips. From beneath the shadow of his hand his eyes regarded her warily.

'I asked you how often you have told a woman you love her and want her very much,' she repeated, and now her voice was hard and brittle. Sliding along the edge of the bed, she stood up and walked away from him to look out of the window at the blue, sun-dazzled sky arching above.

The silence lasted so long that for a while she believed he wasn't going to answer her question and she wondered where she was going to find the confidence to repeat it. When he did speak she jumped a little because he was much nearer to her than she had expected. In bare feet he could move without sound and he was standing right behind her.

'All I can say is that I've never said it before to the woman I've chosen to be my wife. Surely you can infer correctly from that,' he said with a quiet bitter edge to his voice. 'I admit there have been other women before you, but my relationships with them are not your concern. They are over and done with, belong in the past, and. . . .'

'Are you sure?' she asked, turning on him. 'What about the affair you're having with the wife of one of your political colleagues?'

Sebastian couldn't have looked more astounded if she had slapped him across the face. His eyes blazed with a wicked yellow light and his tanned face lost some of its colour.

'What the hell are you talking about?' he grated.

'Your affair with Micaela Gonzalez.'

Frowning, he stared at her for a moment, then with a violent expletive he turned away from her, thrust the fingers of one hand through his hair, made a few paces towards the archway as if he intended to walk out on her, then swung round to stare at her again before striding back to stand in front of her, hands on his hips just where the white swimming briefs he was wearing contrasted starkly with the sun-dark skin of his torso.

'Raquel,' he said tautly. 'I should have known better than to leave you alone with her. She's a garrulous old fool.'

'No, you mustn't call her names. She didn't want to tell me. I made her,' Dawn said urgently.

'But she must have said something to upset you so that you wanted to make her tell you,' he argued coldly.

'It wasn't only Raquel. It was also your good friend and colleague Armando,' she retorted. 'He told me that to get married was a clever move on your part, politically speaking, and then Micaela came and told me that ... that. ...' She whirled away from him to look out of the window again, only she couldn't see anything because those stupid tears would keep misting her eyes.

'So. Now I begin to understand a little your strange behaviour,' he said. 'This is what you had to say to me last night, hmm? This is what sent you rushing up here after you had been talking to Armando. This is what kept you dallying in the bathroom. You've found out that I've been thinking for some time that politically speaking a wife would be an asset and you couldn't swallow and accept that truth. Right?'

'Then it is true?' she cried, swinging back and staring at him as if he was something particularly loathsome.

'Si, it is true, but. ...'

'Oh, how vile you are!' she said in a low accusing voice. 'Vile and cunning and hypocritical. I suppose anyone would have done, any young innocent, gullible girl, and it didn't take you long to find out I'm all of those. The fact that I was in need of help gave you the means to blackmail me into doing what you wanted.'

'Blackmail is a harsh word,' Sebastian countered, his face stiffening with pride.

'I can't think of any other to describe what you've done,' she replied stormily. 'And I hate you for it. I hate you for thinking you could use me to screen from gossip-mongers the illicit affair you're having with Micaela Gonzalez!'

Under the tan he went very pale. A muscle tensed in his cheek and anger flared yellow in his wide open eyes. Then he muttered something virulent in Spanish and again his hand went to his forehead, long fingers stroking across it as if to ease some pain as he closed his eyes.

'*Dios!*' He spoke hoarsely. 'What can I say to make you understand? I thought you would realise....' He broke off, opened his eyes and looked at her directly, no longer angry. 'The problem has been to find someone suitable,' he began slowly. 'Someone who....'

'Someone who could be easily deceived, I've no doubt,' she interrupted him wildly, her voice splintering with the pain of disappointment. 'Someone you could coax and seduce with your kisses and caresses, deceive into believing you want her for herself and not because she would be an asset, politically speaking, of course.' Her voice broke and she turned away from him so that he wouldn't see the tears which had brimmed over and were running down her cheeks.

'Dawn, *querida*, listen to me.' He spoke softly and persuasively and she knew he was very near to her because she could feel his warmth. Then his hand was on her shoulder, lightly.

'Don't touch me!' she cried, flinging round and striking at his arm. 'I can't bear you to touch me!'

Again the yellow blaze in his eyes, and she cringed back, suddenly afraid. But he didn't move towards her. His face was set in harsh, bitter lines and when he folded his arms across his chest she saw the knuckles of his fingers show white through the tanned skin as they gripped his elbows.

'All right, I won't,' he said coldly. 'Not again, not ever unless you come to me and ask me. But I'd like to remind you that you didn't have to marry me. You could have turned down my offer, but you didn't. You decided it was worthwhile going through with the marriage to get what you wanted, to make sure I'd help you find your sister.'

The quiet viciousness of his voice flicked like a whip and her hand went to her mouth in a gesture of dismay as she recognised the truth of his accusation.

'Even when I had doubts about marrying you and withdrew my offer,' he went on, 'you persisted. That was a good act you put on when you came to my room the other night to persuade me to change my mind. Yet you say you're no good at pretending.' His mouth twisted into a sneer and his glance raked her from head to foot. 'No, you aren't any better than I am when it comes to blackmail. You're not above using your feminine wiles and charms to get what you want, and you did want my help to find your sister, remember?'

Before the icy blast of his irony she trembled like a leaf, but his reminder was timely, for she had been so swamped by her own jealous feelings concerning Micaela that she had forgotten Judy.

'So you see there's nothing much to choose between us, is there?' Sebastian drawled rather wearily, and turned away from her to go over to the breakfast tray and test the coffee pot. 'And I suppose in spite of all the accusations you've flung at me this morning you're still hoping I'll fulfil my side of the bargain we made. You'd still like me to take you to Roberto. Right?' He slanted her an ironic glance.

She could only nod, silenced by what she had done with a few angry, unthinking words.

'And in return?' Coldly and sharply his question prodded her and she gave him a quick wary glance. He was standing by the archway now, a tall sturdy man with a beautifully proportioned body shown off by the brevity of the swimming briefs, and he was watching her with haughty eyes. 'You will keep your side of it, even though you hate me? You will continue to be married to me?'

Dawn licked her lips and swallowed an aching rawness in her throat.

'Yes, I will,' she whispered.

'I thought you might,' he replied, and again his mouth twisted in that bitter sneer. 'Then we'll fly to Durango after breakfast. No point in delaying the search any longer.' He made a gesture to the tray. 'The coffee is cold and the *tortillas* are flat and greasy-looking. I'll ask Manuela to make more and we'll eat on the terrace. I'll see you there.'

He went out, and repressing a desire to burst into tears because she felt as if she had lost someone who had become very dear to her, Dawn went into the bathroom.

What had she done? Oh, she didn't understand herself any more. Last night, caught up in the magic spell of passion, she had given herself freely to Sebastian and had taken what he had offered. This morning, with wild hot words born of jealousy, she had driven him from her. Now she was wishing she hadn't said anything to him about other women and had pretended she didn't care if Micaela was still his mistress.

But she had hoped he would deny everything she had accused him of, she thought drearily as she patted her face dry. She had hoped he would tell her his affair with Micaela was over and that she, the pretty bird he had rescued and cared for, came first with him in every way. She had hoped he would have convinced her that she wasn't just a pawn he had chosen to move in some game of chess he was playing with Armando.

He had denied nothing. He had said it was true he had been thinking that a wife would be a political asset and those suspicions she had felt in Guadalajara that the marriage had been planned for some time had been correct. And he had shown how hard he could be accusing her of putting on an act the other night and now holding her to the bargain they had made.

Returning to the bedroom, she put on the skirt of the pale green linen suit. There was a short-sleeved flowered blouse to go with it. Draping the long-sleeved jacket over her shoulders, she regarded herself in the mirror and was surprised to see what she saw. She looked quite elegant, suitable to be the wife of a local politician.

Suitable, suitable. The problem has been to find someone suitable. Sebastian's words pounded through her mind and with an exclamation of anguish she turned away from the pretty, innocent young woman with the waving ash-blonde hair and shining dark-fringed greenish-grey eyes she could see in the mirror.

She wasn't suitable, that was the trouble. She wasn't the sort of person who could be happy with the occasional night of love, knowing that he lived his real life with another woman, was truly intimate with Micaela. She was too proud and possessive to share him, so she would have to leave him.

But first she would let him take her to Durango and then she would leave him somehow. Even if Judy wasn't with Roberto there would be other people at the film location she could ask to help her get out of Mexico and back to Los Angeles. And if Judy was there! Dawn's pulses quickened with excitement. How she hoped Judy would be there. Once she found Judy all her problems would be solved.

On the terrace Sebastian was seated at the table drinking coffee. He was dressed in dark red slacks and a dark red shirt patterned with tiny white flowers. In the sunlight his black hair had the sheen of an eagle's feathers glinting here and there with silver and when he looked up as she took her seat opposite to him his eyes were clear and golden.

'I've managed to find out exactly where Roberto is filming,' he said, his voice cool and impersonal. Carlos approached to pour coffee and place bowls of cereal in front of them. 'He is in a canyon in the Sierra Madre mountains, north of Durango. We'll fly to Durango airport, then hire a car there and drive out to the canyon. You will not mind flying with me again? It won't make you ill?'

'No, I won't mind,' she murmured, stirring sugar into her coffee. If only he was less generous, less thoughtful for her welfare, she wouldn't feel as if she were cheating him by planning to leave him.

But perhaps that was how he wanted her to feel, under an obligation to him all the time, bound to do anything he asked her to do because she owed him so much; the clothes she was wearing, the shelter he had provided for the past few days, the protection he had given her, her life! He had done everything for her a good husband normally did for the woman he had married, even before he had married her, so why shouldn't he demand something in return?

She ate without appetite, thinking with regret that it was her fault they were sitting there in silence, poles apart, two solitudes who had once or twice come very

close to being one. If she had kept her mouth shut instead
of sitting here now, out in the open with Carlos waiting
on them, they would have been together in the intimacy
of her room or his, or perhaps alone beside the pool in
the hall learning more about each other, making love. . . .

Swallowing more hot coffee, she choked and spluttered.
The cup shook in her hand and liquid spilt over the table
and dripped off it. Carlos was there at once, mopping up,
and across the table Sebastian's eyes were hard and
bright, watching her.

'Are you all right?' he asked.

'Yes, thank you,' she muttered, and pushed back her
chair. 'I . . . I've had enough breakfast. Please excuse me.'

He rose to his feet as she did and walked beside her
towards the house. Already the day was hot and the
breeze wafting in from the sea did nothing to alleviate
the humidity, so that it was a relief to step into the coolness of the house.

'Take a change of clothing with you,' said Sebastian
coolly.

'I . . . I've only got the dress I wore yesterday,' she
replied.

'Then take that, and of course, some nightwear.' Was
it her imagination or was there a taunting note in his
voice as he said the last few words? 'We'll have to stay
the night somewhere. From the canyon we'll go straight
to Guadalajara. You'll be able to buy more clothes there.'

'And then will we come back here?' she asked. Better
show an interest in what he planned to do and then he
would think she was going to stay.

'No, we won't be coming back here,' he said crisply.
'I'll go and make sure the plane is ready now. Be prepared
to take off in about half an hour.'

He left her in the hallway and Dawn lingered for a

few minutes beside the pool, watching the fish. So they wouldn't be coming back to this gilded cage where so much had happened between them and where so much more might have happened, where a dream of romance might have become reality. If Micaela hadn't come, hadn't said what she had said. . . .

'Señora.' Carlos was there with Manuela standing behind him. He was carrying a small leather suitcase. 'Manuela says she pack your clothes now. You show her what you want to take, *por favor*.'

'*Sí, sí*,' she nodded, glad to have something practical to do to stop the wandering of her thoughts, and went ahead of Manuela up the stairs.

There wasn't much to pack really, for she had decided to leave the green evening gown behind, hanging in the cupboard, as a reminder to Micaela, who no doubt would use the room when she visited *la casa chica*, that Sebastian had a wife. And by the time Manuela had folded everything neatly and expertly and had packed the small suitcase it was time to go out to the plane.

This time they followed the coastline northwards and Dawn had a panoramic view of golden and black beaches edged by scrolls of white surf which stretched between the coastal towns of Manzanillo, Puerta Vallarta and Mazatlan. The blue ocean looked like crushed satin stitched with silver sequins and white feathers and behind the beaches and the white sparkle of the buildings in the towns the mountains presented a wall of purple-hazed sand-coloured rock, deeply cleft with the dark shadowy green of gorges and canyons.

Sebastian spoke only to point out and name the towns they passed over, and Dawn could think of nothing to say to him because once again the hard inscrutability of his dark foreign face and the abrupt way he spoke to her made him seem very remote and aloof.

After a while he changed course and flew towards the mountains. Slowly a gorge opened up before them and soon they were flying between walls of rock above a glittering river which cascaded down to the sea through the thick green foliage of palms and other trees.

From the dark narrowness of the gorge the plane burst out into sunshine to fly over sun-baked biscuit-coloured land, scattered with sage bushes and shadowed with the weird shapes of giant cacti. The buildings of a town glinted in the distance and soon the plane was descending towards an airport.

There was no problem about hiring a car and once again Dawn became aware of how much Sebastian commanded respect wherever he went. Was it because he was known or was it because he was obviously wealthy? A little of both, she suspected, with the addition of his handsome appearance and charm.

Durango, he told her, had been founded in 1563 and named for Durango in Spain when the Spaniards had searched out valuable mineral deposits, rounded up all the Indians they could, taught them Christianity and had put them to build towns and work in the mines. North of the city, as they sped along a highway towards copper-tinted mountains split by ravines of deep blue shadow he pointed to one of the hills and told her that in it was one of the largest known deposits of iron in the world. In addition there were gold and silver deposits which never seemed to run out in the ore-rich Sierra Madre range.

The harsh, bold landscape fascinated Dawn, Nothing was blurred in this country. Everything was clear-cut, diamond-bright under a deep blue sky across which white cotton-wool clouds drifted lazily.

Then the good road came to an end and they were jolting over a rough surface of a narrower road which twisted upwards through sage brush and cacti, past outcrops of rock, and took them into a wide canyon between bluffs of wind-eroded rock. And there ahead of them was a collection of streamlined trailers, their aluminium walls glinting in the sunlight, the temporary living quarters of the actors, actresses, directors and camera crews involved in making the film.

Sebastian parked the car close to other vehicles which were parked there and together they began to walk over sparse tussocky grass, where some cattle were browsing, in the direction of some wooden buildings. The mountain air was clear and fresh, the temperature ideal for walking. Birds twittered among the few bushes and circling high above the battlemented bluffs of rock which soared against the blue sky Dawn noticed a huge bird. An eagle?

As they drew nearer to the wooden buildings she could see that they formed a street such as she had seen in many Western movies. Verandahs, windows and doorways, representing the stores, saloons, and sheriff's office. There seemed to be some action taking place on the street which was being filmed by two camera crews.

'There's Roberto,' said Sebastian, stopping and pointing to a short wide-shouldered man who was dressed in blue levis, a blue denim shirt and a grey wide-brimmed stetson hat. 'You see how he likes to look the part?' Sebastian added with a touch of affectionate mockery. 'We'll wait here until they've shot the scene, otherwise he'll be angry with us for interrupting them.'

The short man was standing holding the bridle of a black and white pinto pony and was talking to its rider. Whether the rider was a man or woman was difficult to tell because the inevitable levis, checked shirt and stetson were disguising. When the conversation was over the rider wheeled the pony, trotted up to the other end of the street and drew rein to turn the horse round.

Roberto shouted instructions to the camera crews. One crew was just in front of Dawn and Sebastian, slightly above the street so that the camera would have a view of the horse and rider as they approached this end of the street and left the town.

More orders were shouted. The pony began to gallop down the street, urged on by its rider. Dawn saw an actor step from behind a post supporting a verandah, stetson pulled well down over his face. He raised a rifle to his shoulder and appeared to shoot at the rider. Then the thunder of the horse's hooves was drumming in her ears and she was staring in amazed excitement at the rider. For the stetson had slipped back to reveal long corn-coloured hair which glittered brassily under the sunlight as it flowed back from the classically-featured face of the actress who was leaning over the pony's neck.

'It's Judy!' Dawn turned excitedly to Sebastian. 'I'm sure it's her!'

'How can you be sure at this distance?' Sebastian challenged her.

'The colour of her hair,' she said.

'Could be a wig worn by a stunt rider,' he replied dryly. 'You're in the world of illusion now, where nothing is as it seems to be. The riding isn't always done by the actors and actresses who have the leading parts, but by stunt men. But since she's fallen off the horse and the scene seems to be over, we'll go and see, her, hmm?'

Dawn needed no second urging. Stumbling a little in the wedge-heeled sandals which weren't good for running, she ran downhill towards the rider who had got to her feet after her spectacular fall which had apparently been all part of the action.

'Judy!' Dawn called, and the shapely woman in the levis and shirt, who was listening again to Roberto Suarez as he explained something, whirled round in surprise.

'Good grief!' she exclaimed. 'Dawn! How did you get here?' Her blue eyes wide and incredulous in her made-up face, Judy Aylwin ran forward and within seconds the sisters were in each other's arms, hugging each other, crying a little.

'But what are you doing here? Who brought you?' demanded Judy, and turned laughingly to Roberto. 'This is my sister Dawn, Roberto, and I can't think how she got here.'

The short sturdy man with the thick grey hair took Dawn's offered hand in his, an expression of ironic amusement gleaming in his dark eyes. He raised her hand and kissed it.

'I know how she got here,' he said. 'I'm pleased to meet you, little half-sister-in-law. Raquel has told me about you. I talked with her on the phone last night, and she told me about your marriage.'

'You're married?' Judy squeaked. 'To whom?'

'To me,' drawled Sebastian, and she turned to stare at him with round blue eyes. 'And I am pleased to meet you, sister-in-law, and glad also that finding you has been so easy.'

CHAPTER SIX

'AND now we're on our own, tell me how come you're married to that gorgeous hunk of man who happens to be Roberto's half-brother,' exclaimed Judy, pulling the door of the comfortable living trailer closed behind her.

'Is this your place?' Dawn asked, looking round with interest at the long settee berths covered in striped orange and brown moquette set on either side of a table on which a Mexican pottery jar was crammed full of tall grasses and wild flowers.

'Yes, provided by the film producers. Isn't it great? Sit down and I'll make you a nice long cool drink and you can answer that question I asked.'

Judy busied herself at the small refrigerator in the kitchen end of the trailer and Dawn sank down on one of the settees. Orange curtains lifted lazily on the mountain breeze which wafted in through the open windows of the trailer, bringing with it the heady scent of sage.

'First of all I have to tell you why I've been looking for you,' she answered with a sigh. There was no way that she could think of to soften the blow and so she had better come straight out with it. 'Judy, Dad died,' she said quietly.

Judy set down the bottle of soft drink which she had taken from the fridge and turned to stare at Dawn. Slowly her cornflower-blue eyes filled with tears and her perfectly-shaped mouth quivered.

'How?' she whispered. 'When?'

'He died a month ago, but he'd been ill for a while before that. He was knocked down by a car when he was crossing Bloor Street and he didn't get better. I wrote to you to come and see him. He wanted to tell you how pleased he was about your success in landing a leading part in a film. But you didn't come and you didn't write back. Why didn't you?'

'I didn't receive your letter, I guess,' said Judy. 'It must have come after we'd come down here to shoot the film.' A frown creased her high white forehead and she turned back to the bottle of fruit juice and began to pour some into a tall glass. 'Before Roberto offered me this part life was a bit complicated for a while. I had to move out of that flat I was in.' She slanted a wary glance in Dawn's direction, then added, 'I was being harassed.'

'What for? Who was harassing you?' Dawn gasped.

'Oh, a guy I'd met at the film studio when I was working on that first film. Like me he was an extra and for a while we had a thing going between us. Then I found out he was no good, tended to have some parasitic tendencies, wanted to move in with me, shack up with me paying the rent, that sort of lark, so I tried to give him the push. But he wouldn't get off my back. He'd be there every day for some reason or other. So I moved and didn't tell anyone where I'd moved to except the film agency people.'

'What was his name? What did he look like?' demanded Dawn.

'Tall, fair, blue-eyed. Not unlike me. In fact we were often taken for brother and sister, and his name was Leonard Harris.' Judy dropped ice cubes into the pale orange mixture she had concocted, added straws to the two glasses, set one in front of Dawn and slid into the settee opposite. 'You've no idea what a relief it was when I got this part and we moved right down here. I wrote you straight away, but I guess the letter must have got to Toronto after you'd left.' Again her eyes filled with tears and her mouth trembled, 'Poor Daddy, oh, poor, poor Daddy! How I wish I'd known and could have seen him. Tell me all about it, Dawn. Was he in much pain?'

At last Dawn was with someone in whom she could confide and it all came tumbling out—the agony of those few weeks when her father had lingered between life and death. And when she had finished they both cried a little.

'I'm sorry you had to go through it all on your own,' Judy said at last, 'I wish I could have helped. I wish I could have been there. I hope he understood I'd have come if I'd known.'

'Knowing Daddy I think he understood,' Dawn comforted her. 'He kept on saying you had the makings of a real professional entertainer, that you'd put the show before yourself, in the way he had always done. Remember his favourite saying was "The show must go on", no matter what else was happening. He was saying it before he died, and he asked me to come and find you to tell you he was proud you're in show business too and that he'd left you some money.'

'He left you some too, I hope,' said Judy. 'After all, you're the one who kept house and took all the responsibility.'

'Yes, he left me some too, that was why I was able to fly out to Los Angeles to find you.' Dawn's mouth curved in a slightly ironical smile. 'You know, it would have been so much easier if you hadn't told your agents to keep your whereabouts a secret. I could have come straight here.'

'Then how did you find out, and what are you doing married to Sebastian Suarez?' Across the table Judy's blue eyes flashed imperiously. 'Come on, little sister, just what mischief have you been getting up to?'

The story was told slowly, often in answer to prompting questions from Judy—the meeting with Farley at the film studio, the car trip to Manzanillo, the drowning episode, the rescue and all that had happened since then.

'I think Farley is the guy who harassed you, isn't he?' Dawn said eventually.

'He certainly sounds like Leonard from your description, and I did give him a photo of me when we were going about together.' Judy shuddered suddenly and made a grimace of distaste. 'Looking back now I don't know why I had anything to do with him. I was lonely, I guess, when I arrived in Hollywood, looking for friends, and I was easy meat for him.'

'He was very plausible,' murmured Dawn, 'and he knew all about you, even the fact that you'd come to Mexico with Robert Suarez. He suggested to me that you were Roberto's mistress and that was how you got the part in the film.' She gave Judy a level glance. 'Is it?'

'Good grief, no!' Judy looked offended. 'I'll have you know I got the part on my acting ability, good looks and my ability to ride a horse and do my own stunts.' She laughed and added with that touch of self-mockery which had always saved her from appearing to be a show-off, 'Did you notice how naturally I fell off the horse when I was supposed to be shot in that scene?'

'You do ride very well,' replied Dawn with a smile.

'It's me Irish blood showing, as Dad would say,' retorted Judy, and in her turn gave Dawn a level glance. 'Did you really marry your rescuer because he said he would help you to find me and for protection from police questioning?'

Dawn finished her drink before she replied. It gave her time to think up an answer to the question, but in the end all she could say rather weakly was,

'I don't know.' She looked down into the tall glass and swirled the remains of the ice cubes around in it. Through the window came the sounds of men's voices shouting instructions followed by the noise of a heavy vehicle's engines starting up and the rumble of its wheels as it moved away. 'Judy, have you ever been in love?' she added diffidently.

'Me?' Judy's eyes opened wide and she laughed again. 'Dozens of times, ever since I turned fourteen. Fallen out of it the same number of times, too. Why do you ask?' Her face sobered and her eyes darkened to a lovely shade of midnight blue as she considered Dawn's face anxiously. 'Oh, I see, you're not sure if you're in love with Sebastian or not, is that it?'

'Yes,' Dawn whispered. 'The day we were married, yesterday, it all seemed to be so right. I felt very close to him and very happy. And then I found out he'd tricked me into marrying him and that he's going to use the marriage as a screen to cover up a love affair he's been having with a married woman.'

'*Wow!*' Judy's eyes went round. 'This is heavy stuff! So the seemingly romantic hero who rescued you from a watery grave has feet of clay, does he?' she mocked. 'And you can't take it?'

'No, I can't,' muttered Dawn.

'Then what are you going to do?'

'Now that I've found you I'm going to leave him,' said Dawn in a dull flat voice.

'But you've been married only twenty-four hours,' exclaimed Judy.

'I know, but I've worked it all out. Now that I've found you I don't need his help any more. I'm not under an obligation to him now. I can stay with you and come with you when you return to Hollywood. Once I'm back in the States I should be able to establish my Canadian identity pretty soon and then I'll go back to Toronto. If I stay away from him long enough he'll be able to divorce me for desertion....'

'Aren't you going to give him a chance to explain?' cut in Judy sharply.

'I have, and he didn't deny anything,' wailed Dawn miserably. 'He admitted it was true that he'd been think-ing of getting married for some time as a political necessity.'

Judy stared at her with puzzlement clouding her eyes and then she shook her head slowly from side to side so that her golden hair wafted out on either side of her head.

'I don't get it,' she said. 'Do you really want to go back to Toronto?'

'Where else can I go? I've a job there. I was given two months' compassionate leave to settle Dad's affairs and to find you, and I've about three weeks of the leave left. How much longer are you going to be at this location?'

'We shot the last outdoor scene just now as you arrived and we'll be leaving any minute now to drive to Durango to do the interior shots in the studios there. That should take another three weeks to a month, depending on Roberto's temper. He's a perfectionist and will do a scene over and over again to get it right.'

'Then could I stay with you, please, in Durango?' Dawn pleaded.

'I suppose so.' Judy frowned, sighed and then said in a forthright sisterly fashion, 'Look, Dawn, I don't pretend to be competent at marriage guidance, but I do think you're being a fool. You've married a handsome and very wealthy man who happened to save your life. Surely you can turn a blind eye to any philandering he might have done, knowing that as a Mexican he'll always regard his wife and family as sacrosanct?'

'His father was a Mexican and he didn't do that. His half-brother is a Mexican and he's had three wives,' retorted Dawn shakily. 'And the answer is no, I couldn't turn a blind eye, knowing that Micaela. . . .'

'Micaela? Who's she? The married woman you were talking about?'

'Yes.'

'How come you know about her? He wouldn't be fool enough to tell you himself.'

'She told me. She and her husband came to visit Sebastian yesterday and she told me she and he had been in love for years and years and that their affair wasn't over and she thought I should know that.'

'Mmm, sounds to me as if she was suffering from jealousy.'

'Jealousy?' Dawn exclaimed. 'Of whom?'

'Of you, of course, silly.' Judy raised exasperated eyes heavenwards. 'Honestly, Dawn, you're so naïve I'm not surprised you were taken for a ride by Leonard-alias-Farley Harris.'

'But why would Micaela be jealous of me?'

'Because you're Señora Sebastian Suarez and not her. Because he's bound himself legally to you and you're pretty and young and innocent. So she had to get at you somehow. She had to make you jealous. And she did, didn't she?' Judy's laughter was mocking. 'Oh, Dawn, you're really no better than the rest of us. You're finding out the hard way that you can be just as possessive and green-eyed about the man you've fallen in love with as anyone else would be. You know, I wouldn't be at all surprised that if you stick with Sebastian, be the wife he's asked you to be, you'll soon find this Micaela fading out of the picture, fast.'

'Now you sound as if you're on his side,' complained Dawn.

'Side? Whatever are you talking about? Is it a war you're waging with him?' asked Judy, opening her eyes wide.

'Sometimes it feels like it,' muttered Dawn. 'We're so different in every way. He's ... he's so domineering.'

'And you're so liberated,' jeered Judy, then the mockery faded from her face and her eyes grew dark with compassion again. 'You've got it badly, haven't you?'

'Got what?'

'The love bug. Poor little sister, I always thought when I used to hear you talk in that cool dismissing way about men that you'd fall hard when you fell in love. You're going to go through hell if you leave him now, regretting what might have been.'

'The way I see it I'm going to go through hell if I stay with him,' retorted Dawn drearily, 'wondering every time he's away for a night if he's with her.' She took a deep sobbing breath and buried her face in her hands. 'I can't do it, Judy. I can't stay with him knowing about her. I'm just not made that way.'

'If he'd denied your accusations instead of being honest with you would you have wanted to stay with him?'

'Y ... y ... yes, I think so.'

'So when are you going to tell him that you're going to stay with me now that you've found me?' asked Judy, rising to her feet and picking up the empty glasses and taking them over to the sink.

'Then I can stay with you?' said Dawn, looking up.

'You can do what you like, I suppose,' said Judy with a sigh.

'I'll tell him as soon as I can,' replied Dawn with a sniff.

'Well, that might be sooner than you're thinking,' said Judy dryly as she looked out of the window above the sink, 'because he's coming this way right now with Roberto.' She slanted a critical glance at Dawn. 'Better go into the lavatory and do something about your face. It looks like a wet week.'

Only too glad to have a few minutes to herself to re-store her appearance and to regain some of her com-posure before facing Sebastian again, Dawn went into the neat bathroom cubicle at one end of the trailer. There she found some of Judy's make-up and applied it lightly to cover up any signs of weeping. Through the closed door she could hear the quick authoritative staccato of Roberto's voice as he spoke to Judy and her answer, then the slower more drawling voice of Sebastian.

As soon as she re-entered the main part of the trailer her glance went to Sebastian and his leapt to her enquir-ingly, and in spite of the presence of the other two people tension sprang between them immediately. They even moved towards each other as if pulled together by an in-visible elastic cord.

'We are going to Durango, now,' he told her. 'Judy will go with us and we'll stay at the same hotel as her tonight.'

'A good arrangement, don't you think?' said Roberto brightly. 'It is natural when sisters meet after being apart a long time that they want to talk and talk and talk. This way you can do it and this evening we'll all have dinner together and maybe do a little dancing, hmm? A celebration of your marriage?'

'Yes, but....' began Dawn, but her voice was drowned by Judy's. She interrupted to say,

'Sounds a great idea to me—and now if you'd all like to leave for a few minutes, I'll change out of these clothes and put something more feminine on.'

Almost before she realised it Dawn found herself outside the trailer and was walking towards the hired car with Sebastian. Now she must tell him, she thought, while they were alone and unobserved.

'Sebastian.'

'Mmm?'

'There's something I have to say to you.'

'Then say it.'

'Now I've found Judy I don't need your help any more.'

'So?' he drawled.

'I don't feel under any obligation to keep my side of our bargain.'

He stopped in mid-stride and she stopped too, bracing her shoulders and lifting her chin in readiness to do battle with him, knowing that there was going to be a battle when she saw the cold light in his eyes.

'Meaning you're going to desert me?' he accused.

'I suppose you could put it like that,' she replied.

'I *am* putting it like that,' he said harshly. His glance drifted over her slowly and insultingly and she felt the hot colour of shame creep up into her face. 'I wonder where I ever got the idea that you're different from any other woman I've ever known?' he grated bitingly. 'I wonder why I imagined you'd keep a bargain if you made one? You've turned out to be no more trustworthy than the next bitch!'

She flinched at that and although she felt an urge to hit him for insulting her she managed to keep her hands down and return his unpleasant stare.

'If you think like that about me you'll be glad to be rid of me,' she countered coolly.

Again his glance went over her, but this time it

touched and possessed her, and she felt the familiar thrill of excitement surge through her and weakly acknowledged that if he moved towards her and took her in his arms she wouldn't have the strength to resist. But he didn't move. He just stood there with his hands in his trouser pockets, his dark hair lifting slightly in the breeze which wafted down from the high bluffs of rock, his eyes hard and clear, devoid of expression as he studied her.

'But I don't want to be rid of you, *chiquita*,' he said softly. 'You're very necessary to me and I'm not going to let you leave me.'

'You can't stop me from leaving you,' she retorted. 'I'm not trapped in the gilded cage now without money and clothes. I'm going to stay here with Judy while she has to be in Durango and then I'll go to Hollywood with her.'

'I see. Then I'll have to stay in Durango too and go with you when you travel north,' he replied coolly with a shrug of his shoulders. 'It isn't my idea of how to spend our honeymoon, but, if it's what you want to do, then we'll do it.'

'It won't be a honeymoon,' she stormed at him. 'Oh, why can't you understand I don't want to be with you any more? This marriage isn't going to work, so we might as well end it here and now. Stop tormenting me and let me go.'

'I'm not letting you go,' he said between taut lips. 'And don't think for one moment it's torment only for you. I'm in torment too.'

He swung away from her and strode over to the car to unlock the trunk ready for Judy's cases, then he slid into the driver's seat, banged the door shut and sat there, staring straight ahead of him.

He was in torment too! What had he meant by that?

That being married to her when he was in love with Micaela was torment for him? Then why had he married her? Oh, they must have been both out of their minds yesterday to go through with this strange marriage, both of them driven to madness by the wild sweet passion born of physical desire.

Somehow she must think up another way to leave him, preferably before he had a chance to make love to her again. All the way to Durango plans sifted through her mind while she kept up a conversation with Judy. But it wasn't until she was standing in the beautiful baroque entrance hall of the hotel which had once been the elegant eighteenth-century home of a Spanish aristocrat that she hit on a plan which had a good chance of working.

In a rack on the reception desk there were pamphlets advertising the various attractions of the area surrounding Durango and the trips which tourists might take and among the pamphlets was one setting out the schedule of the long-distance buses which passed through the town on the way to Cuidad Juarez at the border between Mexico and the State of New Mexico in the United States.

After making sure that Sebastian and Judy were both too busy booking rooms for the night to notice what she was doing Dawn took one of the schedules. All she needed now was money, and she could borrow that from Judy, she was sure.

The room she was to share with Sebastian was reached from the gallery, which was supported by pillars of creamy-coloured stone and edged by a balustrade of polished golden wood. The colour scheme of terra-cotta red walls and cream paintwork which prevailed in the hallway was continued in the wide airy room. Two double beds were covered with cream-coloured silky quilts and the window opened outwards on to a delicately designed wrought iron balcony from which plants of colourful bougainvillaea tumbled in a blaze of purple.

Judy's room was next door and could be reached through a communicating door. Dawn waited until Sebastian had gone into the bathroom to have a shower and then she unlocked the communicating door, opened it and stepped into the other bedroom.

'Judy, you've got to help me get away from here, now,' she said urgently.

Judy, who was in the process of taking clothes from her suitcase to hang them in the closet, stared at her.

'Why?'

'Because I . . . I . . . can't stay with Sebastian any longer. I can't share a room with him here. He might—he might. . . .' Her voice trailed away.

'He might make love to you and persuade you to stay with him, I suppose,' Judy finished for her. 'Look, Dawn, why don't we sit down and talk about this sensibly?'

'No. There's no time. A bus on its way from Aquascalientes to the border stops at this hotel to pick up passengers in exactly twenty minutes. All I need is the money to pay for my fares and meals. When I get to the border I can change on to another bus and work my way northwards across the States to Toronto. If I'd had the money before I'd have left long ago, or at least tried to find you on my own. But Farley stole all mine, so please will you lend me some?'

'I've only got traveller's cheques,' Judy stalled.

'Well, you should be able to change those down at the hotel counter,' argued Dawn stubbornly.

'And you might not get a seat on the bus. Often they're booked up weeks ahead,' retorted Judy.

'If I can't, I'll go to the airport to try and fly out. Please, Judy, come on!'

'Okay, okay.' Judy picked up her handbag and followed Dawn to the door. Then she stopped short. 'You're going to need something warmer to wear if you're going to sit up all night on the bus and you're going to need a bag of some sort to carry the money in, and though I still think you're a fool for doing this, I suppose I'd better provide you with something more suitable in the way of clothes. Here, get into these.' She pulled some jeans out of her suitcase, a neatly-checked shirt and a thick-knit cardigan.

'Thanks,' said Dawn, giving her sister a kiss, and began to strip. In a few minutes she was dressed in Judy's clothes, having to turn up the bottoms of the jeans a little because they were too long. Then slinging her shoulder bag over her arm, she went with Judy down to the hall.

There was no problem about cashing the cheques nor in booking a seat on the bus, and soon she was leaving the hotel to board the bus which was waiting in the courtyard.

'Stall for as long as you can, please, Judy,' she pleaded. 'Let him come and ask you where I am then pretend you don't know. You're good at pretending.'

'Okay,' sighed Judy. 'You always were stubborn. But good luck—and write to me. Let me know when you reach Toronto. Write care of this address.' She pushed a piece of paper into Dawn's hand.

Dusk was covering the mountains with a blanket of deep purple as the bus ground its way through the streets of Durango and swept out on to the northbound highway. Soon the sky was completely dark and hung with brilliant stars. Sitting by a window, Dawn stared out. Over six hundred and seventy miles to Cuidad Juarez and it was now six-thirty. She would be at the border at about eight o'clock in the morning, all being well. . . .

· And Sebastian? Where would he be then? What would he do when he found she had gone? How long would Judy be able to stop him from finding out that his wife of a night and a day had flown the coop?

For the next hour or so the questions tormented her while she tried to find answers to them. The bus roared along the Central Highway, climbing hills and dipping down the other sides. A smiling stewardess came round with soft drinks and coffee. Dawn took a soft drink and sipped at it. Her stomach gurgled noisily and she remembered she had had nothing to eat since that late breakfast on the terrace at *la casa chica* with Sebastian. At the first stop she must get out and buy something to eat, if there was anything to buy.

Gradually the monotony of the ride had a soporific effect on her. Her head began to sway, so she tilted the seat into a reclining position and settling her head on the small cushion which the stewardess brought to her she dozed intermittently.

At the first stop she roused herself and left the bus to buy a hamburger at the restaurant near which the bus had parked and when she returned to her seat she settled down hoping to sleep all night. In sleep there would be forgetfulness, for she must stop thinking about Sebastian, remembering how close to heaven she had felt whenever he had held her in his arms, how nearly she had realised a dream of romance.

That was how she must think of it, her stay in Mexico, as a vivid colourful dream. She must pretend it hadn't really happened. But the trouble was she was so bad at pretending. And how could she account for the changes in herself, for the new awareness of her body and of its needs? Sebastian had awakened her to a new way of life, had quickened desire in her, and if she had stayed back there at the hotel in Durango he would have satisfied that desire. . . .

She moaned softly, covering her face with her hand, closing her eyes tightly to try to blot from her mind's eye images of Sebastian and trying not to hear the words of love he had spoken to her only that morning. *Te quiero muchisimo. I love you very much.* And she had spurned those words, answered them with a cold mocking accusation which he hadn't denied.

Mercifully she slept, stirring sleepily to change her position whenever the bus stopped but not waking properly until the grey light of dawn filtered into the interior of the bus showing up the forms and faces of the other passengers. Sitting up, Dawn lifted the window blind and looked out. The sand dunes of a desert, grey and desolate, lifted in rolling curves to meet a cold grey sky streaked with pale silvery light. Then slowly the sky flushed with rose-pink light and the shapes of the dunes became rimmed with gold. Fascinated, she watched the greyness change to a dark red which gave way to pale rose which faded gradually to a bleached glittering yellow as the sun came up over the horizon. As far as she could see smooth billows of sand stretched, a sea of yellow waves shaped by the wind, under the blue arch of a cloudless sky.

People stirred, stretched their limbs, opened their eyes, sat up and began to talk. A different stewardess came round with soft drinks and coffee. Dawn took coffee this time and heard an American voice behind her say it wouldn't be long before they would be crossing the border. That was where she might meet her first difficulty, she thought, when she was questioned by the U.S. Customs. She might be asked to show some form of identification. If she was she would just have to tell them the truth, that her passport and her tourist card, all her forms of identity, driving licence, social insurance card had been stolen.

Now that the night was over and she was on the point of leaving Mexico she didn't want to go and was wishing she hadn't left Durango so precipitously last night. She wished she had taken Judy's advice and had stayed, stuck it out, showed Sebastian she could be the wife he wanted her to be, and pretend Micaela didn't exist.

Overwhelmed suddenly by regret, she sat slumped in her seat, looking out but hardly seeing the glittering new buildings of the busy port of entry, Cuidad Juarez, named after Benito Juarez, Mexico's great national hero, the poor Zatopec Indian who had become President and had given the country a sense of nationhood.

She would have to go back to Durango. Dawn wasn't conscious of making the decision, she just knew she would have to get off the bus before it crossed the border into the States and take the next bus back if she could get on it. She would have to sink her pride since she guessed Sebastian wouldn't sink his. She would have to go and show him again that she wanted him and what was more that she loved him enough to accept him the way he was.

With a grinding of gears the bus turned off the street along which heavy traffic was streaming towards the bridge which crossed the Rio Grande into the U.S.A., and glided into the courtyard of a bus station. With other passengers who were not going to the States she trooped off the bus and went into the building where the booking office was situated. There was a line of people waiting to book seats, so she joined it, thinking there would be time to get breakfast once she had the ticket.

, She stood there in a sort of daze, thinking of Sebastian, wondering if he would still be in Durango or whether he would have flown back to Guadalajara. It never occurred to her that he might have come after her, but it worried her that she couldn't get him out of her mind. It was almost as if he were trying to get in touch with her over the long distance which separated them. She had never had much time for telepathy, but there in the busy bus station she began to wonder if there were wavelengths between the minds of people.

'Excuse me, *por favor*.' The stewardess from the bus was there speaking to her, in rather garbled English. 'You are Señora Suarez? Señora Sebastian Suarez?'

'*Si*.'

'There is a message for you, at the information desk over there.'

'Oh, thank you, *muchas gracias*.'

Dawn left the line of people and went over to the desk where a young man with a swarthy face and a thick droopy black moustache eyed her with interest.

'You are Señora Sebastian Suarez?' he asked.

'*Si*.'

'I have a message here for you from a Señor Roberto Suarez in Durango. He ask you to call this number straight away.' He handed her a piece of paper on which a number was written. She stared at it, feeling herself go cold with dismay. Roberto calling her? Something must have happened to Judy for him to go to the trouble of asking the bus people to make contact with her.

'Could you, would you please show me how to make a long-distance call?' she asked the young man. 'I'm not quite sure.'

He studied her over the top of the desk for a few

minutes, then smiled and drew his own phone towards him.

'I get the number for you, *señora*,' he told her.

'Thank you.'

Within a few minutes she was listening to a ringing tone, then heard the phone lifted at the other end and gasped with surprise when she heard her sister's voice.

'Judy, it's Dawn. I received a message from Roberto asking me to call that number. Oh, Judy, are you all right?'

'Yes, yes, of course, I'm fine. It's Sebastian. He's been badly hurt. He took off in his plane early this morning and it crashed near the airfield. Roberto asked me where you'd gone and if it was possible to get in touch with you, so I told him. Oh, Dawn, you've got to come back! You made an awful mistake....'

'I know, I know. I was coming back. I'll get the next bus. Judy, is he ... will he ... oh God, Judy, he won't die, will he?'

'I don't know. Roberto seems to think it's touch and go and that's why he wants you to come. Don't take the bus —fly back. There's a regular service from there to here. Let me know when you arrive and I'll come to meet you.'

Tears were wetting Dawn's cheeks as she replaced the receiver and turned to thank the young man.

'You have trouble, *señora*?' he asked softly. Like Sergeant Moreles, like all young men with a smattering of Latin blood in their veins he couldn't hide his interest in a person of the opposite sex, couldn't prevent it from showing in the gleam of his dark eyes. Dawn wiped the tears away with the back of her hand.

'Yes. Seb ... my ... my husband,' how strange it was to say that word, 'he's been hurt. I have to go back to Durango. Could you tell me how to get to the airport?'

'*Si señora.* I will get you a taxi. Would you like me to call the airline and make a reservation on the next flight?'

'Oh, could you?' She smiled. 'I'd be very grateful if you could.'

'To see you smile like that I would do anything, *señora,*' said the young man gallantly.

It was surprising how kind everyone could be when you were obviously in trouble, thought Dawn later as aboard a fast-flying jet plane she looked out at a serene, hot blue sky. The weather was so clear she could see the land far below, copper-coloured mountains wrinkled with ages and riven by deeply shadowed dry canyons.

The journey back took little more than an hour. From the airport she phoned the hotel in Durango to let Judy know she had arrived and then took a taxi into the town.

Both Judy and Roberto were in the hotel foyer. Judy came forward to kiss her, but Roberto didn't offer to embrace her, just looked at her with dark angry eyes and said,

'First let me say I am glad you have enough feeling for Sebastian to turn around and come back. Second I have to tell you it is believed he has severe concussion. He hasn't recovered consciousness yet.'

His hostility after the warmth and kindness shown to her by perfect strangers was like a blast of icy wind. It braced her and she put her shoulders back and lifted her chin at him.

'Can I go and see him?' she asked.

'Of course. I'll take you to the hospital in my car.'

'How did it happen?' was her next question as they all turned and went out of the hotel into the courtyard.

'A matter of poor communications at the airport. There was something on the runway when he was taking

off and he swerved to avoid it and the plane tipped over.'
Roberto shrugged. 'I am told it could have been worse.
The gas tank could have blown up and he could have
been burnt to death. As it is,' he waggled one hand from
side to side in a dramatic gesture, 'it is touch and go.' He
opened the back door of his car and indicated to her that
she should get into the back seat. 'So get in the car,
pronto,' he ordered, 'for who knows, we may be too late.
He may have passed on.'

The dark melancholy expression on his face, his Mexican acceptance of death chilled her and she was glad of
Judy's comforting hand as they sat side by side in the car
as it wove through the cobbled streets of the old Colonial
part of the town, past high white walls with narrow
windows covered by iron grilles.

That feeling she had had on the bus this morning, the
feeling of closeness with Sebastian, hadn't been only
imagination, then. At that time he had been in trouble
on the runway at the airport, had crashed his plane and
had been knocked unconscious, and she had felt his
spirit touch hers across all those miles and had decided to
return to him.

The hospital was new, bright and clean. Sebastian was
in a room by himself in the intensive care ward. Roberto
introduced Dawn to the nursing Sister with whom he
held a brief conversation in Spanish.

'She says you can go in to see him,' he said, turning to
Dawn. 'He regained consciousness an hour ago and the
tests show that he is likely to make a recovery. The concussion is not as severe as they had thought.' He saw the
expression of heartfelt relief on her face and his eyes
softened. 'But he is very restless, she says. He wants to
get up, so he has been put under heavy sedation. She asks
you not to stay too long and not to excite him because it

is important that he sleeps. Judy and I will wait for you.'

'Thank you.'

Dawn pushed open the double doors of the small room
and stepped in quietly, memories of the times when she
had visited her father in hospital rushing into her mind.
There was very little difference really between this room
and the room he had been in. The same antiseptic smell,
the same high bed covered in stark white, the same bedside locker with water carafe and glass. The only differences were the blinds covering the window to prevent
the brilliance of the sunlight from disturbing the patient
and the patient himself, black-haired, olive-skinned, a
man in his prime.

Quietly she crept to the bedside. Although his eyes
were closed there was a frown line between the shapely
dark eyebrows and his mouth was taut as if with pain.
Yet there were none of the usual signs of illness in the
room. No intravenous drip hung by the bed. No bandage
curved about his head. In fact the only sign of damage to
him was the thin red line high on his cheekbone where it
had been cut by a piece of ice—or had it been glass?—
when she had thrown lemonade at him.

She stared down at the silky blackness of the hair
clustering about his frowning forehead, at the thick
lashes lying against his cheeks, at the proud curve of nose
and the tough angle of jaw, at the lines that laughter
had etched beside the corners of the broad-lipped mouth,
and felt such a surge of love go through her that she had
to turn away in case she touched him.

Over to the window she went to peep through the slats
of the Venetian blind at the distant splash of colour
which was the flower beds in the hospital yard. So this
was what it was like to be not merely in love with someone but to love him so much you were willing to ignore

the differences between you and him, just to be with him.

'So you've come back.' His voice was a little thick and she turned quickly, went to the bed and sat down on a chair beside it. From under heavy lids the drug-dulled golden eyes surveyed her coolly. And finding her throat too full of tears for speech she could only nod. Sebastian pulled a hand from under the bed-clothes and reached out to touch her cheek with a long forefinger. 'Just making sure you're real,' he explained in a murmur with a mocking quirk to his lips. 'I've been having hellish dreams.'

'How do you feel?' she asked in a small squeaky voice which was all she could manage to produce right then.

'Damned stupid,' he muttered. 'After all those years of flying to make a mistake like that!' He added something in Spanish which she didn't understand and closed his eyes again.

The frown had gone from his forehead and his mouth was relaxed. He was going to sleep fast. She had known from past experience of sitting with her father that it would be like this, the occasional flashes of lucidity followed by long silent periods of apparent sleep. But she couldn't help feeling disappointed because he had said so little and had shown no sign of being glad to see her.

She sat there for about fifteen minutes hoping he might wake and speak to her again. But he didn't, and then the nursing Sister came in, smiled benignly and with pleasure because her patient was sleeping and indicated that she should leave.

Dawn spent the rest of the day at the film studio watching the interior scenes being shot. She was glad to have something fascinating to watch, admiring her sister's acting ability and being thrilled to know that the leading man in the film was a well-known star. Having her name associated with his was bound to help Judy's career even though in this, her first leading role, she wouldn't receive star billing.

In between the shots Judy sat with her and told her the story of the film. Like all the other Westerns Roberto had made the plot was one of revenge and about the hunting down by the laconic hero of the man who had ravished his innocent sister, only to discover that the sister of the villain was the woman he had fallen in love with—the part played by Judy.

When the filming was over for the day they went back to the hotel and Roberto phoned the hospital for news of Sebastian. Dawn found it irritating having to get the news second hand through Roberto, but there wasn't anything she could do about it because she didn't have enough Spanish to converse with the hospital staff.

'He is sleeping again, thank God,' Roberto told her, 'and the Sister says she doesn't think there is much point in us going to visit him until tomorrow. She says thanks to his splendid physical condition he is making very good progress and tomorrow we should see a big difference.'

'So it wasn't touch and go, as you suggested,' said Judy shrewdly. The three of them were sitting in the hotel lounge having pre-dinner drinks, sitting at a round table upon which a candle flickered while all around them the sound of other people talking and laughing rose and fell, waiters moved smoothly and discreetly and the Latin-American music played by a trio of men on guitars, drums and flute provided a sensually romantic background.

Roberto's dark eyes glinted mockingly as he looked up.

'Maybe not, but it brought her back, didn't it?' he countered. 'Why did you run away, little half-sister-in-

law? If you love him, and I think you do, why leave
him?'

'I'd found out why he had to get married,' muttered
Dawn defensively.

'Had to get married? Sebastian had to get married?'
exclaimed Roberto. '*Dios*, what nonsense is this? Please
explain.'

Dawn looked across at Judy for advice.

'Go on,' Judy urged. 'Tell him what you told me about
this Micaela woman.'

'Micaela?' Roberto's voice was sharp. 'You mean
Micaela Gonzalez?'

Dawn nodded, and then somehow it all came out in
a rush because she found Roberto, like his sister Raquel,
was kind and sympathetic and not at all hostile after all.
When she had finished he gazed at her with a sort of
tender mockery.

'And you say Sebastian didn't deny he had been con-
sidering getting married for political reasons? But of
course he didn't, because that part was very true, he
had,' Roberto explained. 'You see, for some time now
Armando Gonzalez has been using his wife's preference
for Sebastian to ruin Sebastian's career by spreading
rumours, making out that they were having a torrid love
affair.'

'But I don't understand. Why would Armando want to
do something like that?'

'In the game of politics as in the game of love all is
fair, I guess,' replied Roberto with a shrug. 'Armando and
Sebastian are rivals in the Legislature and Armando
would very much like to see Sebastian defeated in the
next election, then his own road to power would be
clearer. So for the past year or so he has been conducting
a very subtle mud-slinging campaign. On the face of it he

and Sebastian are good friends, but rumour says he is being cuckolded by Sebastian. Thus he gets all the sympathy and Sebastian gets all the mud. Understand now?'

'I ... I ... think so.' Dawn felt very bewildered. 'But there must have been something going between Micaela and Sebastian for Armando to have a basis for his rumours, and Micaela told me herself they were in love with each other years ago.'

'Ah, that woman, she's nothing but a tramp,' said Roberto scornfully, his eyes flashing. 'And she would cause trouble for anyone who turned her down. Now Sebastian isn't a saint by any means, and perhaps he did have a little fling with Micaela years ago and again when she turned up in his life three years ago. But when he realised any association with her was going to ruin his reputation he dropped her like a stone into a puddle, just like that.' Roberto made an expressive movement with one hand. 'But it wasn't enough to stop the spread of rumours, because she followed him about, went wherever he was going, and that was when it was suggested to him that a wife, marriage to a nice innocent young woman, would help. But he didn't like the idea. You know why?' Roberto gave Dawn a quick underbrowed glance.

'No.'

'He likes to be free, to come and go as he pleases. But he said he would think about it. And think about it is all he has done for months on end with the rumours getting worse, and when my mother or my sister ask him why he isn't doing anything he shrugs and says he can't find any woman he wants to marry, that all the women he knows are either married already, aren't pretty enough or aren't virgins.' Again Roberto gave Dawn another underbrowed look and the twinkle of mockery was back in his eyes. 'I think now you must have guessed why, when you turned up in his life, he acted fast, perhaps a little too fast. Perhaps he should have explained first, hmm?'

'Then you're sure he isn't still having an affair with Micaela?' said Judy, leaning forward urgently. 'You see, Roberto, that's what's really sticking in Dawn's throat, as it would in mine.'

'I'm sure Micaela isn't his mistress, nor is she likely to be, and she probably said she was to cause trouble between you and Sebastian, to destroy his marriage to you before it had really started. Who knows, maybe Armando put her up to it? But I can't be sure he doesn't have a mistress or isn't going to have one.' He shrugged and gave Dawn another long look, this time a very serious one. 'That is something you'll have to ask him yourself. And now shall we have dinner?'

Dawn was glad she was able to share Judy's bedroom that night, because she knew that if she were alone she would be in torment. There was so much to think about, so many questions to be answered yet.

'Did you tell Sebastian where I'd gone last night?' she asked as soon as the lights were out.

'No, but he guessed,' Judy replied with a rueful laugh.

'And when he realised I'd gone what did he do? What did he say?'

'He shrugged his shoulders, behaved as if you did it all the time and said nothing to me, but after dinner I didn't see him again.'

'Do you know where he was going when the plane crashed?'

'Not really. Roberto said he thought Sebastian was going to Guadalajara to some sort of meeting. He was surprised, though, that he was leaving so early in the morning.' There was a short silence, then Judy said diffidently, 'Are you going to stay with him now you've come back?'

'I want to, oh, I want to,' whispered Dawn into the darkness, 'but I'm not sure he'll want me any more. He wasn't exactly overjoyed when he saw me.'

'Well, give him a chance, love,' said Judy. 'He's got concussion and isn't feeling too good. Wait until he's got over that crack on the head and he'll be showing you what he really feels about you.'

But during the next few days Dawn wondered whether she would ever be close to Sebastian again. It was true that he was making a rapid recovery according to the nursing Sister and doctors with whom she could only communicate through Roberto and they were predicting that he would be released from hospital soon and able to go home with her. Whenever she went to see him he was out of bed dressed in a dark green dressing gown sitting in a chair by the window of his room and he talked with her lucidly, but never once personally. Nor did he ever once attempt to greet her with an embrace.

It was as if an invisible screen had come between them through which she could find no way of penetrating, and after a while she began to wonder if the concussion had caused him to forget how close their relationship had been or had been in process of becoming before Micaela and Armando had interfered. Had he forgotten he had once told her he loved her very much? She longed to ask the doctor if it were possible that the concussion had caused some slight amnesia, but couldn't because of her lack of Spanish.

In the end she confided her worry to Judy.

'Why don't you ask Roberto to ask the doctor for you?' suggested her sister.

'I don't like to,' muttered Dawn.

'Why on earth not?'

'I don't want him to think there's anything wrong between Sebastian and me. Will you ask him for me?'

'Okay, anything to help the course of true love along,'
sighed Judy.

And so Roberto duly consulted the doctor and reported
back.

'It seems there is a possibility that Sebastian may be a
little forgetful for a while, but gradually, once he is back
in his home and among familiar things and people, he'll
remember. And since he's made such good progress and
you seem to be a dutiful attentive wife the doctor is going to release him tomorrow,' said Roberto. 'I've told
Sebastian and he's asked me to make arrangements for
you both to fly to Manzanillo where you'll be met by
Carlos and taken to *la casa chica*.' Roberto's mouth
twitched humorously. 'And there, little half-sister-in-law,
you can have him all to yourself to nurse and cosset for
the next two or three weeks.'

The flight to Manzanillo didn't take very long, but it
was an unhappy one for Dawn because she sensed Sebastian's frustration because they weren't returning home
in his plane with him at the controls. She knew that already he was in the process of negotiating to buy another
plane, because that was one of the few subjects he had
discussed with her during her visits to the hospital.

She was glad, therefore, when the plane touched down
and even more glad to see Carlos waiting for them in the
arrival lounge of the airport, but she couldn't help feeling
hurt when Sebastian chose to sit in the front seat of the
car next to his houseman and talk to him exclusively during the drive down the coast, their common language of
Spanish shutting her out deliberately, she felt.

When they arrived at the house she couldn't help comparing their return with the time she and Sebastian had returned from Guadalajara after their marriage. Was it only a week since they had walked with their arms about one another and Sebastian had talked about where they would live and the children they would have? Oh, God, it seemed like another lifetime. Had it happened to two other people?

As had been predicted by the doctor, Sebastian was tired after the journey and went to his room to rest. Dawn spent the remainder of the afternoon trying to fill in time by reading, by walking on the beach, wondering what wives who had no housework or cooking to do did with their time. What had Polly Moore done when she had lived here? Written in her diary, she supposed.

Well, she had a husband who had been ill to look after, but how could she do that when he had Carlos to wait on him, when his cold direct glance set her at arm's length, no, further away than that, told her more or less that he didn't care if she was there or not?

The day dragged to its close. Sebastian didn't come down for dinner but ate in his room. When the house was quiet Dawn trailed disconsolately up the stairs and paused at the archway leading to his room. The bedside lamp was on, its lights shafting across the bed, gleaming on the bare shoulders of the man who lay there, his back turned to her, apparently asleep.

Memories of that other night she had come to this room to turn off the light caused her throat to ache. They were too much for her, and with a little moan of torment she turned away to go to her own room, to hide in the bathroom and cry in regret for what might have been.

'Dawn.' He spoke quietly and she turned hesitantly to look back at him. He was sitting up, leaning back against the pillows. 'Did you want something?' he asked.

I want you. The words stormed through her mind, but she didn't say them. Instead she spoke as quietly as he had, mindful of the doctor's instructions. On no account must he be excited.

'I'm going to bed now. I just thought I'd look in to see if you're all right.'

'Don't overdo it, will you?' he said, his mouth curling unpleasantly.

'Overdo what?' she replied uncertainly.

'The part of the concerned wife. I know you came back only because Roberto told you I might not live....'

'I didn't!' she flared suddenly, stepping into the room, going right up to the bed so she could see him more clearly, forgetting that she mustn't answer back and cause him to get excited. 'I was coming back anyway. I was waiting to book a seat in a bus coming back to Durango when I got the message to phone Roberto.'

'You really expect me to believe that?' The curve to his mouth was really cynical now.

'It's true,' was all she could say. 'I ... I ... found out on that bus ride that I ... I ... love you in every way a woman can love a man and I want to stay with you, live with you, so I came back.' Suddenly she was down on her knees beside the bed, her feelings for him sweeping aside her pride. 'You've got to believe me,' she whispered, 'you've got to!'

'I don't see why. You didn't believe me when I told you I love you,' he retorted, looking at her with eyes that gleamed with golden light between thick black lashes.

He hadn't forgotten, then. Or had the return to this place where he had confessed his love for her reminded him, cleared his mind of whatever cobwebs the concussion had shrouded it in?

'That was because I didn't understand about Micaela,' she whispered, and he opened his eyes wide.

'Ah, so you understand about her now, do you?' he taunted. 'Yes, Roberto told me all about Armando's mud-slinging campaign and how Micaela followed you about.'

'You listened to Roberto, you believed him,' he said angrily. 'Yet when I tried to explain to you you interrupted me with wild accusations.'

'It was because I was upset and confused. . . .'

'*Dios*, are we back to that?' he groaned, thrusting fingers through his tousled hair. 'Are you always going to be upset and confused by what I do and say, by what I've said and done in the past? You said when I first asked you to marry me that it was crazy because we come from different cultures and have different values. I knew what you meant, but I hoped,' his voice shook with the intensity of his feelings, 'I dared to hope that we would love one another enough to compromise and overcome those differences. But you made no effort. . . .'

'I did, I have now,' she cried. 'Although I don't think I can compromise with you if you have a mistress. Oh, don't you see, Sebastian? I want to be your mistress as well as your wife!'

The words rang out in the silence of the house and she realised suddenly how alone they were, able to show each other how they felt whenever they liked and wherever they liked, and that was exactly what they were doing, even though to an outsider it might sound like a quarrel to end all quarrels.

'And isn't that what I wanted you to be in the first place, ever since I held you in my arms that night to comfort you after you had nearly drowned?' he countered softly. 'Only I came up against that remarkable innocence of yours and to my own surprise fell in love with you.'

'But only after you'd decided I was suitable to be your wife,' she accused, and then cried out loud as he lunged across the bed, grabbed her by the shoulders and pulled her down onto it. For a few minutes there was a wild struggle as she attempted to break free, but in the end his superior strength won. Pressing her back against the pillows, he loomed over her, his eyes gleaming with menace in a taut angry face.

'So we come always to the same *impasse*, you little wildcat,' he muttered between set teeth.

'Let go of me! You're hurting me, and the doctor said you're not to. . . .'

Sebastian said something viciously rude about the doctor and in the next moment smothered her mouth with his and at once the flame went dancing along her nerves to light the fuse of desire.

'Are you going to let me finish explaining without any more interruptions?' His voice was a soft snarl and his lips moved against her cheek.

'I'll try,' she gasped, for already his fingers were seeking the sentient hollows of her throat. 'The doctor said you're not to get excited, so yes, I'll listen.'

'Then I'll begin, although it doesn't please me to learn that you're complaisant only because the doctor told you to humour me,' he retorted, and flicked her cheek with a hard admonishing finger as he rolled away from her, but kept a hold on her arm with the long fingers of one hand, fingers which began to move seductively on the thin skin of her wrist even as he began to speak.

'I have told you, *chiquita*, that I wanted you from that first time I held you in my arms. I've also told you that I have always held to a certain principle in my life, and that was never to sleep with a virgin unless I married her first. I went to Guadalajara believing you might be gone by the time I returned and the problem would be solved for me. But you were still here in my house when I came back, and it was then during the days of your sickness that I realised you were someone I wanted to care for and look after for the rest of my life, and I made up my mind that if I could in some way persuade you to stay with me a little longer I would propose marriage to you. The idea of marrying you as a political necessity never entered into it. I was in love, madly and impossibly in love for the first time in my life and I never gave anything else a thought. Do you believe me?'

He rolled back on to his side and leaned over her again, a dark tormenting threat to her peace of mind.

'I want to,' she whispered, and raised a hand shyly to touch his cheek. At once his hand covered hers and he drew it across his face to his mouth to kiss the palm of it and fold her fingers over the kiss.

'Then Sergeant Moreles came and pushed me over the edge of commitment, I proposed to you much sooner than I intended—and the courtship of one rebellious Irish girl by a Mexican *macho* was on.' His laughter mocked himself. '*Dios*, it was hard work for a man like me who has always enjoyed his freedom to court someone like you. I had doubts, as you know, and withdrew, my pride up in arms because of the way you behaved. But if you hadn't come to my room that night I'd have found some way the next day to stop you from leaving and I'd have started courting you all over again. And it seemed to go well after that. I thought we were very close when we came back here and found the Gonzalez' waiting for us.'

'We were, we were. I felt it too,' she whispered. 'If only they hadn't been here!'

'But they were, and our love was put to the test far too soon. I tried to explain to you, but you were too hurt to listen, so I thought that if I took you to find Roberto, showed you I was really willing to help you find your sister, it would be enough to prove to you that I love you, but it wasn't. You ran away and that night I found out the hard way, sweating in torment, alone in the hotel bedroom at Durango, what it is to love a woman in every possible way, and I knew I couldn't let you go. I kept torturing myself with visions of what might be happening to you on that bus, wondering who might be beguiling you as Farley did. I went through hell, and that is why I went to the airport and took off. I had some crazy notion of flying north and intercepting you at the border.' His voice was muffled suddenly as he buried his face against her shoulder. 'You see what you'd done to me? You'd sent me out of my mind! If I'd been thinking in a normal rational way I wouldn't have made that stupid mistake on the runway, I'd have been listening to the air traffic controller and not thinking of you. What more proof do you want that I love you?'

'None, none,' she cried, winding her arms about him. 'Oh, I know about going through hell, too. That night on the bus—I didn't know until then how much it's possible to miss someone, to ache to be with him, hear his voice, touch his hand, so I turned back. But at the hospital you were so cold and indifferent I thought you must have forgotten you'd once told me you love me.'

'I'd forgotten nothing,' he said softly. 'But I was unsure about you. Roberto said you'd come back as soon as you heard I'd been hurt and I didn't want that to be the only reason for your return.'

'It wasn't. I was coming back. Oh, what do I have to say or do to convince you?' she said urgently.

'I'll show you in a few minutes, but first there is something which has to be cleared up between us. If necessary I'll give up politics, if that is what is required to prove to you that I married you for love and only for love. Is it what you want?'

'You would really do that for me?' she exclaimed, drawing back from him so she could see the expression on his face in the lamplight, and his mouth twisted wryly.

'Is it always going to be like this between us, I wonder? Are you always going to be testing me? *Si, chiquita,* I would really do that for you, as my mother gave up her career to live with my father and he ruined his political career to live with her. Have you forgotten I am a child born of love?'

In silence Dawn stared at him, facing him as they lay on the bed. Once more she was aware of a struggle between them, but it wasn't a struggle to find out who had the superior strength. It was a test of love. Who could love the most, he or she? Could she do what he was offering to do? She could do more. She could love him enough to refuse to let him make the sacrifice. She could love him enough to accept his word that there was no affair between him and Micaela and that he loved her in every way it is possible for a man to love a woman without him having to give up his career to do it.

'No, that isn't what I want, at all,' she whispered.

'Then what is it you want?' he retorted softly.

'To stay with you, live with you and love you.'

'For ever?'

'For as long as you want me.'

'Are you sure?'

'Yes.'

'Then convince me.'

Willingly she put her lips to his, eagerly she raised her hands to ruffle the hair at the back of his neck, invitingly she pressed herself against his hard, pulsing body. At once he responded, arms tightening about her, lips bruising hers in passion.

'Now say it,' he whispered. 'Say it after me. *Te quiero muchisimo, querido.*'

'*Te quiero muchisimo, querido.* I love you very much, darling,' she said, and again his lips took possession of hers and the torment of their mutual desire swept them along on its flood, obliterating all that had happened in the past from their minds and taking no account of tomorrow. Love was now, in the present, and it was theirs.

Harlequin
Announces the
COLLECTION
EDITIONS
OF 1978

Harlequin's Collection 1.25

ANDREA BLAKE
Night of the Hurricane

Harlequin's Collection 105 1.25

ANNE WEALE
If This Is Love

stories of special
beauty and significance